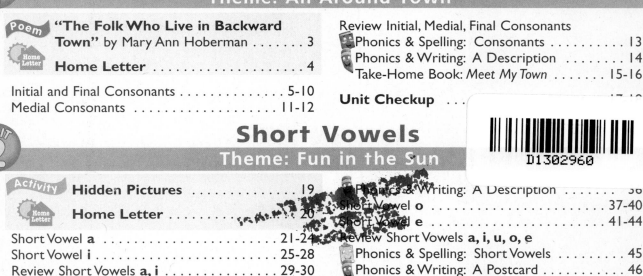

LEVEL B

CONTENTS

This book belongs to:
Ms. E. Rodriguez

Initial, Medial, Final Consonants

UNIT 1

Theme: All Around Town

Short Vowels

UNIT 2

Theme: Fun in the Sun

Long Vowels

UNIT 3

Theme: On Wings and Wheels

Compounds; Le Words; Hard and Soft c, g; Blends; Y as a Vowel; Digraphs; R-Controlled Vowels

UNIT 4

Theme: The World Outside

UNIT 5 — Contractions, Endings, Suffixes
Theme: Blasting Off

UNIT 6 — Vowel Pairs, Vowel Digraphs, Diphthongs
Theme: Dinosaur Days

UNIT 7 — Prefixes, Synonyms, Antonyms, Homonyms
Theme: Make It, Bake It

Unit 1 pg-3-18 F&B 30 copies

Read Aloud

The Folk Who Live in Backward Town

The folk who live in Backward Town
Are inside out and upside down.
They wear their hats inside their heads
And go to sleep beneath their beds.
They only eat the apple peeling
And take their walks across the ceiling.

Mary Ann Hoberman

▶ **Talk about some of the funny things in the poem.**

THINK! Why is the town named Backward Town?

Home Letter

Dear Family,

During the next few weeks, we're going to be learning about letters and sounds at the beginning, middle, and end of words. We'll also be talking about our neighborhood and community.

At-Home Activities

Here are some activities you and your child may enjoy doing together.

▶ Make a list of places to visit in your town. Ask your child to draw a picture of his or her favorite place in town.

▶ Take a walk through town with your child. As you go, point out words on signs, buildings, and stores. Read the words and have your child identify the letters for the beginning and ending sounds.

Book Corner

You and your child might enjoy reading these books together.

Cool Ali
by Nancy Poydar
Ali's drawings help her neighbors beat the heat on a summer day in the city.

How to Get Famous in Brooklyn
by Amy Hest
Janie records all of the things that happen in her neighborhood until the wind blows away her papers.

Sincerely,

> **Say** the name of each picture. **Print** the capital and small letters for its beginning sound.

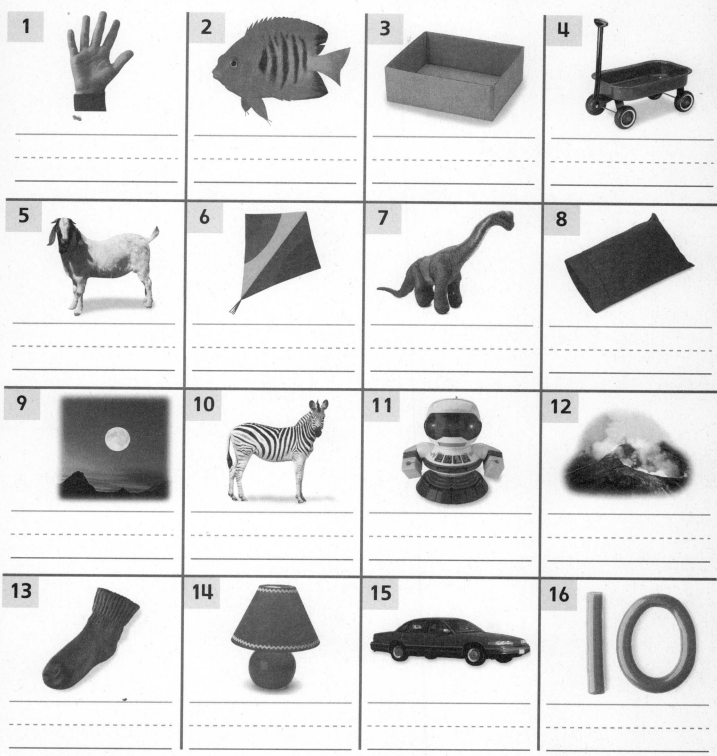

1

2

3

4

5

6

7

8

9

10

11

12

13

14

15

16

Say the name of each picture. Print the letter for its beginning sound. Trace the whole word.

1	2	3	4
ie	ig	un	all

5	6	7	8
in	ap	ire	ive

9	10	11	12
am	et	ug	og

13	14	15	16
ap	eb	oo	ey

Lesson 1
Initial consonants: Spelling

Ask your child to name another word with the same beginning sound as each word pictured.

Say the name of each picture. Print the letter for its ending sound.

Say the name of each picture. **Print** the letter for its ending sound. **Trace** the whole word.

1  ma	**2** we	**3** do	**4** be
5 sai	**6** cu	**7** su	**8** bu
9 ha	**10** lea	**11** bo	**12** dru
13 ti	**14** bow	**15** bir	**16** ja

Home

Ask your child to name the pictures whose names have the same ending sounds.

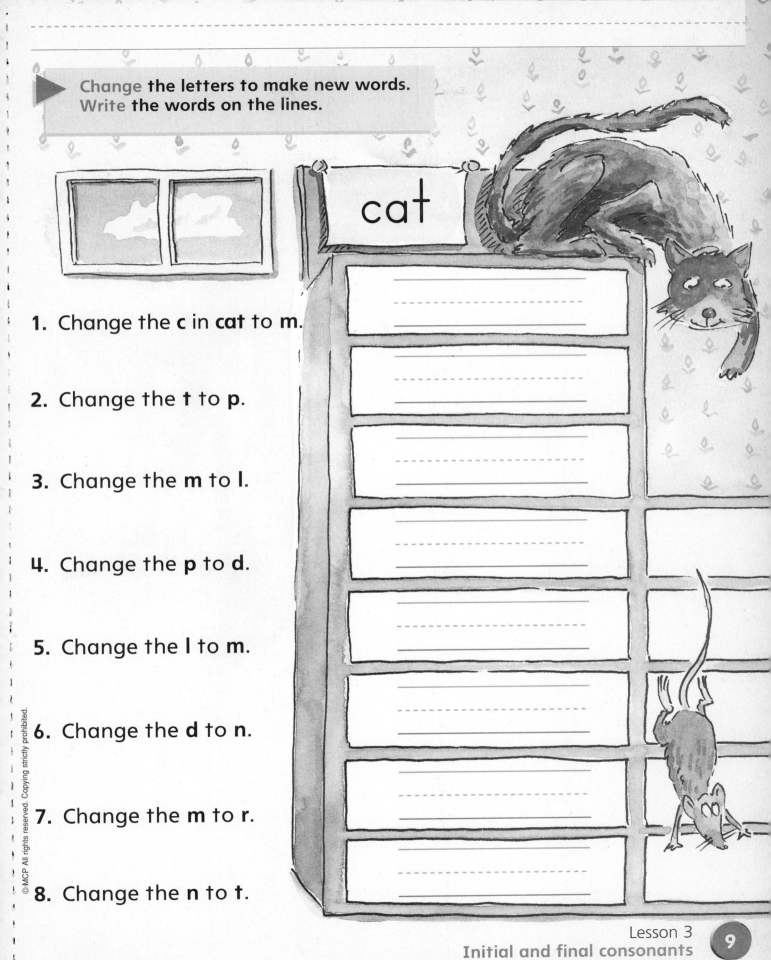

Change **the letters to make new words.**
Write **the words on the lines.**

cat

1. Change the **c** in **cat** to **m**.

2. Change the **t** to **p**.

3. Change the **m** to **l**.

4. Change the **p** to **d**.

5. Change the **l** to **m**.

6. Change the **d** to **n**.

7. Change the **m** to **r**.

8. Change the **n** to **t**.

Say the name of each picture. **Print** the letter for its beginning sound. Then **print** the letter for its ending sound. **Trace** the whole word.

1   o

2   a

3   u

4   e

5   u

6   o

7   i

8   a

9   e

10   o

11   a

12   e

Lesson 3
Initial and final consonants: Spelling

Home

Say a word and have your child think of another word that has the same beginning or ending sound.

Say the name of each picture. Print the letter for its middle sound.

1

2

3

4

5

6

7

8

9

10

11

12

13

14

15

16

Medial consonants: Phonemic awareness

► **Say** the name of each picture. **Print** the letter for its middle sound. **Trace** the whole word.

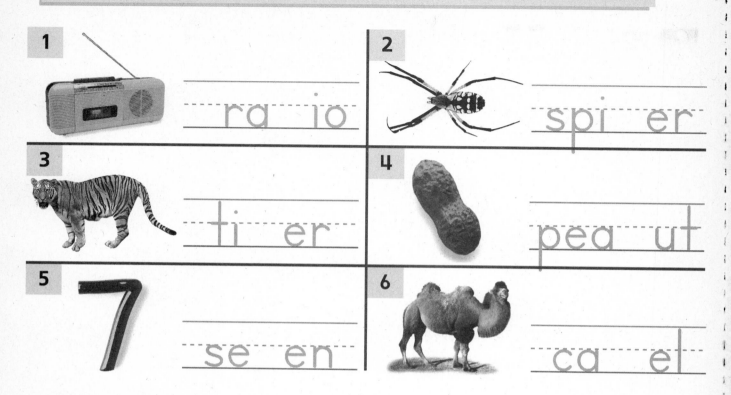

1 ra io

2 spi er

3 ti er

4 pea ut

5 se en

6 ca el

► **Say** the name of each picture. **Print** the letter for its middle sound. **Trace** the whole word. **Do** what the sentences tell you to do.

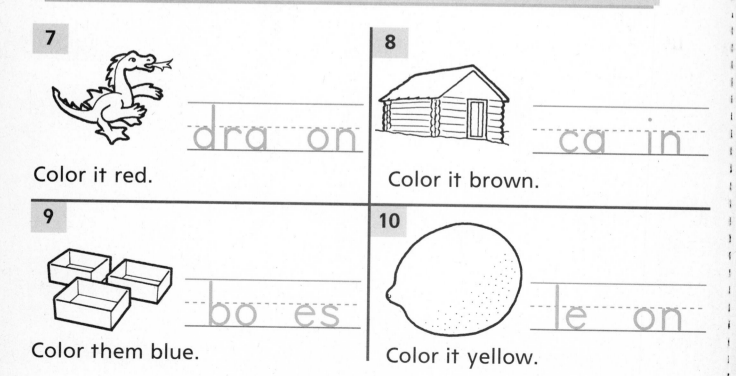

7 dra on
Color it red.

8 ca in
Color it brown.

9 bo es
Color them blue.

10 le on
Color it yellow.

Home Ask your child to write the words on the page with the same medial sounds.

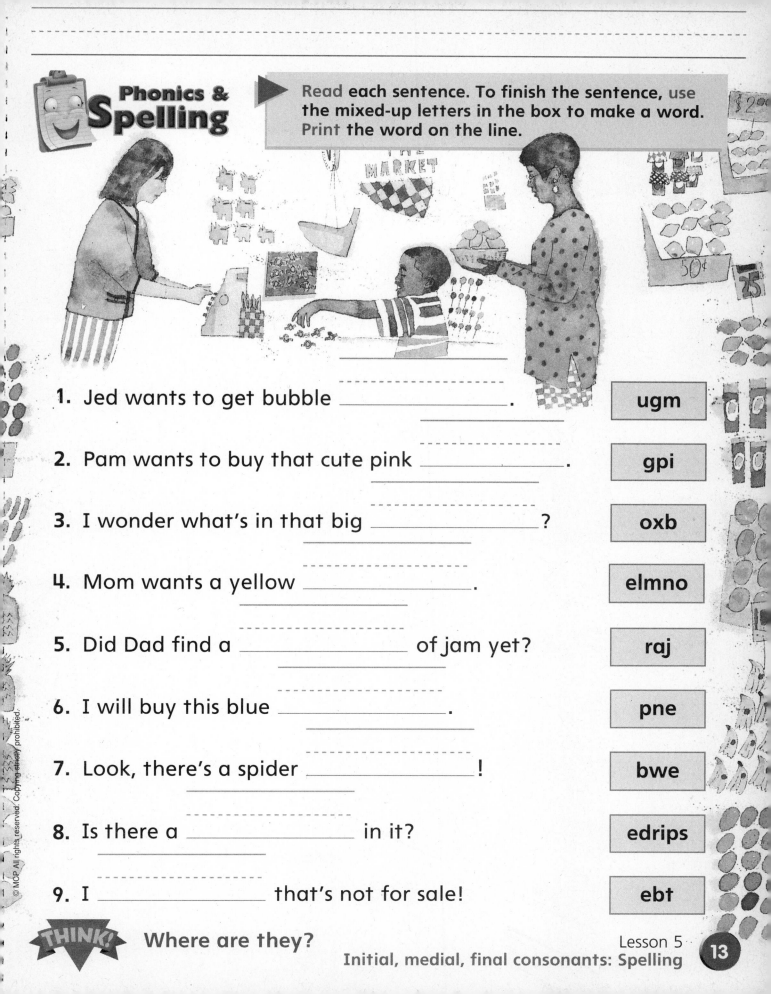

Phonics & Spelling

Read **each sentence. To finish the sentence, use the mixed-up letters in the box to make a word. Print the word on the line.**

1. Jed wants to get bubble _____. **ugm**

2. Pam wants to buy that cute pink _____. **gpi**

3. I wonder what's in that big _____? **oxb**

4. Mom wants a yellow _____. **elmno**

5. Did Dad find a _____ of jam yet? **raj**

6. I will buy this blue _____. **pne**

7. Look, there's a spider _____! **bwe**

8. Is there a _____ in it? **edrips**

9. I _____ that's not for sale! **ebt**

THINK! Where are they?

Lesson 5
Initial, medial, final consonants: Spelling

13

Phonics & Writing

Write about a place in your neighborhood that you like. Tell where it is and what you do there. Then tell why you like it. Use some of the words in the box.

gum	store	spider	ride	park
yard	bus	house	library	box
school	porch	web	play	robot

Book Corner

Mrs. Tuck's Little Tune
by Cass Hollander

Mrs. Tuck's tune is passed from one person to another until the whole community is humming it.

Ask your child to name the letters at the beginning, middle, and end of some of the words he or she wrote.

Who is in your family?
What do you like to do
together?

8

Meet My Town

This book belongs to:

1

Meet all my family. This is my
sister, Meg. That is our dog,
Tiger. Have I left anyone out?

6

ART FAIR

This is my school. You can find
me here five days a week. I
painted the red dragon.

3

Meet my dad. He drives a taxicab all around the town. I like to go with him.

2

Oh, yes! Meet me—Jim! How do you like my pictures?

7

My town is not very big, but it has a lot of shops. You can get fish or milk. You can get a drum or a dress.

4

Meet my mom. She plays music and talks on the radio.

5

Say the name of each picture. **Fill in** the bubble beside the letter for the beginning sound of the word.

1.
○ b
○ g
○ d

2.
○ k
○ m
○ y

3.
○ w
○ r
○ t

4.
○ w
○ l
○ m

Say the name of each picture. **Fill in** the bubble beside the letter for the ending sound.

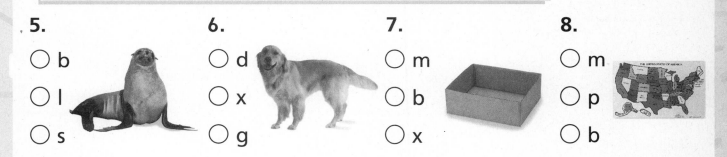

5.
○ b
○ l
○ s

6.
○ d
○ x
○ g

7.
○ m
○ b
○ x

8.
○ m
○ p
○ b

Say the name of each picture. **Fill in** the bubble beside the letter for the middle sound.

9.
○ r
○ c
○ b

10.
○ c
○ t
○ r

11.
○ m
○ n
○ l

12.
○ r
○ d
○ l

Circle **the word that answers the riddle.**
Print **it on the line.**

1. Jam goes in me. I am a _____.

jar
car
farm

2. I rhyme with **drum.** I am _____.

gas
gull
gum

3. A spider spins me. I am a _____.

web
well
wet

4. I say "oink." I am a _____.

big
pig
fig

5. I come after six. I am _____.

seven
tiger
robot

6. I rhyme with **fox.** I am a _____.

bag
box
bell

7. You can write with me. I am a _____.

pet
peg
pen

8. You can ride in me. I am a _____.

cabin
wagon
lemon

Lesson 7
Initial, medial, final consonants: Checkup

With your child, take turns making up riddles using the words on the page.

UNIT 2

Short Vowels

Theme: Fun in the Sun

► Find the hidden pictures of things you can have fun with.

THINK! Which hidden thing would you want to play with most of all? Why?

Home Letter

Dear Family,

Your child will want to share with you what we'll be doing in the next few weeks—learning to read and write words with these short vowel sounds.

a clap

e bend

i skip

o hop

u run

The names of many things that we do for fun contain short vowel sounds. In this unit, we will be learning about ways to have "fun in the sun."

At-Home Activities

Here are some simple, fun activities you and your child can do at home to practice short vowel sounds.

▶ Play a riddle game with your child. Think up a riddle whose answer is a short vowel word; for example: "I am what you do with a song. What am I?" (sing)

▶ Play "Concentration." Print words with short vowel sounds—two words for each sound—on individual cards or slips of paper. Shuffle the cards and place them face down. A player turns over two cards at a time. The object is to find two cards with the same vowel sound.

Book Corner

You and your child might enjoy reading these books together.

Almost Famous Daisy
by Richard Kidd
Daisy searches for inspiration when she enters the Famous Painting Contest.

Jo Jo's Flying Side Kick
by Brian Pinkney
Jo Jo demonstrates his strength and self-confidence as he tries to earn a yellow belt in his tae-kwon-do class.

Sincerely,

Fast, fast, fast.
My taxicab goes fast!
I can slow my cab down
As I get close to town.

RULE

If a word or syllable has only one vowel, and it comes at the beginning or between two consonants, the vowel is usually short. You can hear the short **a** sound in **fast.**

▶ **Circle the name of each picture.**

1		2		3	
hat	ham	bag	hat	camp	lad
hand	had	bat	bad	lap	lamp

4		5		6	
sad	back	cat	cap	and	an
bag	bat	cab	can	at	ant

7		8		9	
mat	man	cat	can	mad	ram
pan	map	cab	cap	rack	mat

Lesson 8
Short vowel a: Picture-text match

21

▶ **Draw a line through three words that rhyme in each box. Lines can go across, up and down, or on a diagonal.**

1

ram	cab	gas
sad	ham	tag
bad	fan	yam

2

ax	lap	hat
wax	map	can
bag	nap	had

3

dad	tap	pal
bat	sat	cat
mat	pan	cap

4

tax	fat	tag
mad	wag	tab
bag	pad	sag

Lesson 8
Short vowel a: Phonograms

Home

Help your child think of another word to add to each group of rhyming words.

Find words in the box that **rhyme** with each child's name.
Print the rhyming words above or below each child's picture.

cat	ham	dad	fan	jam	van	hat	bad
sad	pan	yam	mat	can	bat	had	ram

1

Dan

2

Pat

3

Pam

4

Tad

1. I am Sam, and my cat is _____.　　camp　Pat　cart

2. Pat likes milk and _____ food.　　class　sat　cat

3. She eats a lot, but she is not _____.　　van　fat　lamp

4. She likes to lick my _____.　　hand　gas　band

5. Pat likes to sit on my _____.　　lap　ham　Sam

6. Pat does not like to have a _____.　　gap　bath　rack

7. She runs away as _____ as she can.　　fast　class　bass

8. I _____ always find her.　　can　past　fast

9. She takes a nap on a _____.　　mast　mat　fat

10. She takes a _____ on Dad's lap.　　ran　sat　nap

11. I _____ happy that Pat is my cat.　　can　am　as

THINK!　**Does the cat like Sam? How do you know?**

Home　Ask your child to reread the sentences and name the short a words.

We will visit the city.
We will sit in the stands.
We will see the ball hit.
We will cheer with the fans.

▶ Circle **the name of each picture.**

1

sack
milk
mill
tap

2
mitt
fat
mat
mill

3
wind
tag
wig
wag

4
lap
lips
nap
dill

5
bag
pig
fig
pat

6
hill
bill
sill
hat

7
tax
six
fix
sat

8
bill
bit
hat
bib

9
wink
sank
sink
pink

Color the parts of each ball with rhyming words the same color.

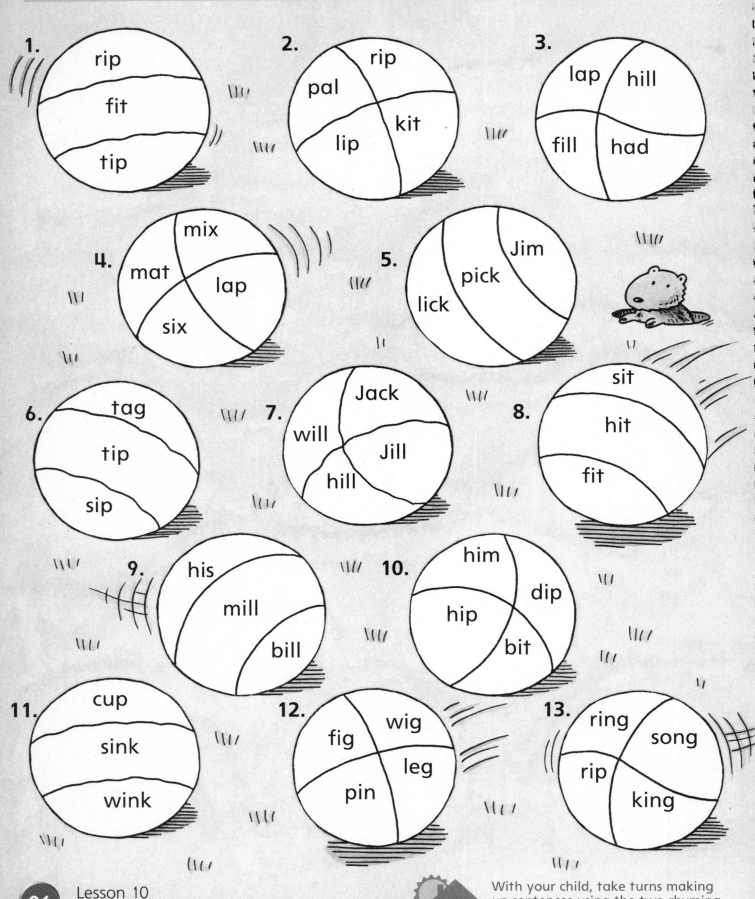

1. rip / fit / tip

2. rip / pal / kit / lip

3. lap / hill / fill / had

4. mix / mat / lap / six

5. Jim / pick / lick

6. tag / tip / sip

7. Jack / will / Jill / hill

8. sit / hit / fit

9. his / mill / bill

10. him / dip / hip / bit

11. cup / sink / wink

12. wig / fig / leg / pin

13. ring / song / rip / king

Home

With your child, take turns making up sentences using the two rhyming words on each ball.

Print the word in the box that names each picture.
In the last box, draw a picture of a short vowel
word. Print the picture name.

1	2	3	4

5	6	7	8

9	10	11	12

Circle the word that answers each riddle. Print it on the line.

1 It can swim. What is it?

----

fast   fish

fix   fat

2 We drink it. What is it?

----

mitt   man

milk   mat

3 It comes after five. What is it?

----

sink   sad

sat   six

4 It rhymes with **bill.** What is it?

----

hit   hat

hill   ham

5 Lunch goes on it. What is it?

----

dad   dish

dig   did

6 It has a funny tail. What is it?

----

pin   pig

pal   pat

7 It fits on a finger. What is it?

----

rank   rat

rip   ring

8 A baby wears this. What is it?

----

bib   bad

bill   bat

9 I play ball with it. What is it?

----

mat   mitt

map   mix

Home

Ask your child to name a word that rhymes with the answer to each riddle.

> **Circle the word that finishes each sentence.**
> **Print the word on the line.**

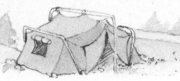

1. We are going to take a _____. trap trip tan

2. Dad will look at the _____. map win cab

3. Pam will _____ the snacks. dish fix mix

4. We will _____ a tent. pick pack ram

5. Will our _____ fit in the van? sit big bags

6. My dog Wags can _____ with me. bat sit bib

7. Wait! Where is the _____? cat pat pick

> **Write a sentence to finish the story. Use some of the short a and short i words in the story.**

_____

_____

_____

_____

► **Look** at the picture. Then **follow** the directions below.

Here's what to do.

1. Color the hills green.
2. Circle the pan.
3. Color the boy's cap black.
4. Draw a box around the ax.

5. Make an X on the man's hat.
6. Color the little fish blue.
7. Draw fins on the big fish.
8. Color the bag yellow.

Help your child list all the short *a* and short *i* words.

I can have fun,
Running in the sun.
Playing in the mud
With my friend Bud.

▶ **Circle** the name of each picture. **Print** the vowel you hear in the word you circled.

1		2		3	
cap	cup	gas	gull	Dick	duck
kit	_____	gum	_____	dad	_____

4		5		6	
can	cup	as	bun	tug	tip
cap	_____	bus	_____	bug	_____

7		8		9	
but	nut	sun	sum	tab	bin
nap	_____	dim	_____	bat	_____

Lesson 13
Short vowel u: Picture-text match

31

Find the word in the box that names each picture. Print it on the line.

bun	cup	rug	bus	bug	sun
gum	hug	hut	tub	jug	duck

1

_____

2

_____

3

_____

4

_____

5

_____

6

_____

7

_____

8

_____

9

_____

10

_____

11

_____

12

_____

Lesson 13
Short vowel u: Spelling

 Home

Have your child make up silly sentences with words from the box that rhyme. Include other rhyming words.

Read the words in the box. Print a word in the puzzle to name each picture.

run	bus	tub
bun	bug	rug
cub	sun	nut

Across →

2.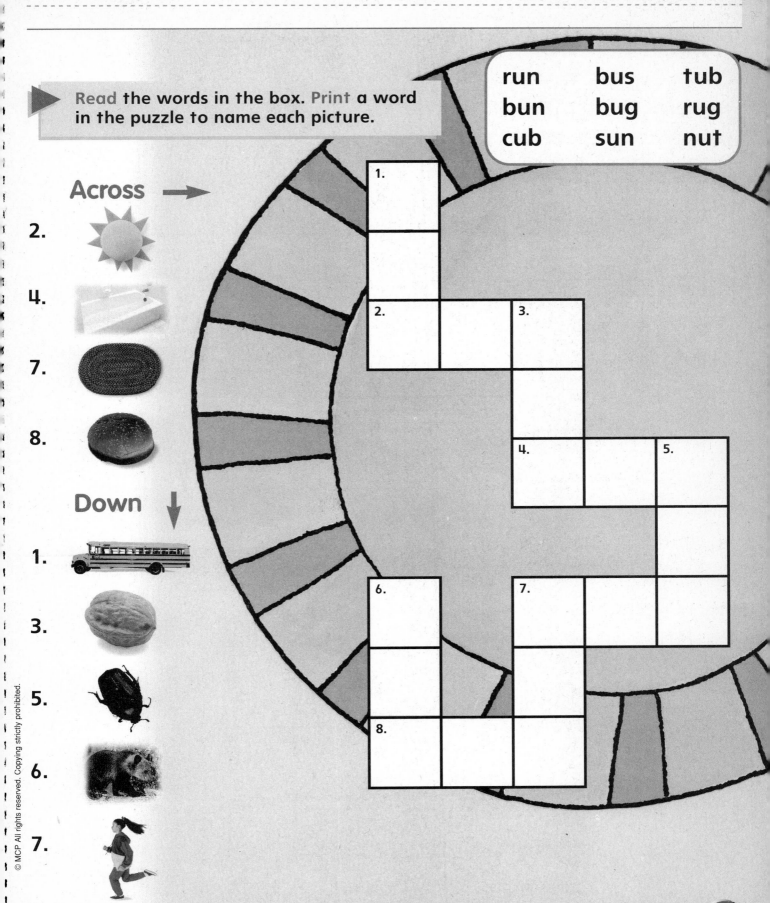

4.

7.

8.

Down ↓

1.

3.

5.

6.

7.

Circle the word that will finish each sentence. **Print** it on the line.

1. Today there was a fuss on the _____.

run
bus
must

2. A _____ jumped on Gus.

us
bug
hug

3. Gus jumped _____.

run
cup
up

4. Then it jumped on _____.

bus
hug
Russ

5. I saw the bug _____ on the window.

just
jump
rust

6. It was _____ a little bug.

just
cup
up

7. It liked to _____ up and down the window.

rug
run
cup

8. The bug _____ like to ride on the bus.

run
us
must

THINK! What would you do if you were on the bus?

Phonics & Reading

▶ **Read** the story. **Print** a short **a**, **i**, or **u** word from the story to finish each sentence.

Ball Games

Balls are used in many different games. In some games, you hit the ball with a bat. Then you run fast! In other games, you jump up and hit the ball with your hand. In some games, you can hit the ball with anything but your hand! In yet another game, you can throw the ball, kick it, or run with it.

You can play ball games just about anywhere. You don't need much to have fun—just some friends and a ball!

1. You can hit a ball with a _____ or your _____.

2. When you hit the ball, you _____ fast!

3. In one game, you can throw the ball, run with it, or _____ it.

THINK! Name the games in the story.

Phonics & Writing

▶ Write **about a game you like to play. Don't give its name. Have your friends guess the game. Use these words and your own.**

run
jump

bat
hit

cap
kick

him
fast

tag
fun

Lesson 15
Review short vowels a, i, u: Writing

Home

Talk to your child about favorite games you played as a child.

Put it in the pot,
Shake it 'til it's hot.
Pop! Pop! Pop!
It's time to eat popcorn!

▶ **Find** the word in the box that names each picture. **Print** it on the line.

top	doll	lock	sock	hot	pot
Tom	pop	mop	box	rock	fox

1 _____

2 _____

3 _____

4 _____

5 _____

6 _____

7 _____

8 _____

9 _____

10 _____

11 _____

12 _____

Circle the name of each picture.

1

fix
cob
fox
six

2
pot
top
tap
pit

3
bill
sill
dill
doll

4
fox
fix
box
bat

5
dog
dug
dig
pot

6
rock
sit
sack
sock

7
pig
pop
pup
pat

8
lag
log
bug
lot

9
luck
lock
lick
lack

10
mop
map
mud
milk

11
hat
hit
hot
hut

12
fix
tax
ax
ox

 Home

Have your child find the pictures on this page and on page 37 whose names rhyme.

Help the frog hop to the pond. Look at each picture.
Write the name of each picture on the line.

| top | dog | box | sock | |
| lock | rock | log | fox | pot |

1

○ The fox is not on the log.
○ The fox is in the log.
○ The fox is on the log.
○ The fox is under the log.

2

○ Rob lost his sock.
○ Rob sat on a big rock.
○ Rob is on the big log.
○ Rob has a big rock in his hand.

3

○ The dog ran to the box.
○ The mop is not in the box.
○ I will hop on the log.
○ See the doll in the box.

4

○ I got the mop for Don.
○ Jill has the small top.
○ The small top is on the mop.
○ The top is in Bob's hand.

5

○ The hot pot is on the table.
○ Dot is not holding a hot pot.
○ Dot is holding a hot pot.
○ The milk in the pot is not hot.

Lesson 17
Short vowel o: Words in context

Home

Ask your child to read a sentence that is not pictured, and draw a picture for it.

Come on Fred and Jen,
Let's get wet!
It's a good way to cool off—
The best I've found yet!

▶ **Say** the name of each picture. **Print** the name on the line.

1

2

3

4

5

6

7

8

9

10

11

12

Print the name of each picture. Then do what the sentences tell you to do.

1

_____

2
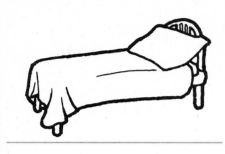
_____

3
_____

4
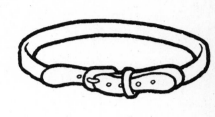
_____

5
_____

6
_____

Find the bed.
Color it red
and blue.

Find the jet.
Color it black.

Find the nest.
Color the
eggs blue.

Find the tent.
Color it yellow.

Find the belt.
Color it green.

Find the vest.
Color it red
and black.

Lesson 18
Short vowel e: Spelling

Home

Ask your child to find the names of two colors on this page that have the short e sound.

Fill in the bubble below the word that will finish each sentence. Print the word on the line.

1. My name is _____.

   men   Jeff   jet
   ○   ○   ○

2. I want to get a _____.

   bet   pet   yet
   ○   ○   ○

3. I would like a pet dog _____.

   rest   west   best
   ○   ○   ○

4. I will _____ take care of my pet.

   help   bell   nest
   ○   ○   ○

5. I can take it to the _____.

   vet   bet   set
   ○   ○   ○

6. I will make sure it is _____.

   get   fed   bed
   ○   ○   ○

7. It will need a good _____.

   bed   nest   best
   ○   ○   ○

8. I will _____ it in and out.

   jet   test   let
   ○   ○   ○

9. I can dry it when it's _____.

   net   wet   set
   ○   ○   ○

10. I will _____ it if I get it.

    sled   pet   west
    ○   ○   ○

11. I might name my pet _____.

    Pepper fed   set
    ○   ○   ○

12. I will _____ Ned about my pet.

    sell   tell   fell
    ○   ○   ○

THINK! Why would Jeff make a good pet owner?

Lesson 19
Short vowel e: Words in context

43

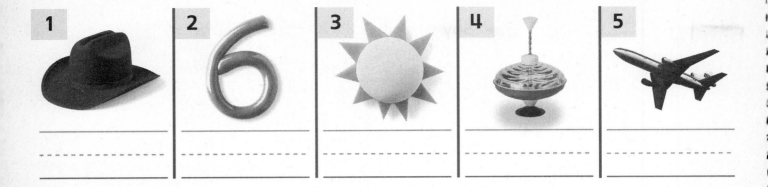

1	2	3	4	5

▶ **Print yes or no on the line to answer each question.**

6. You can sit in a tent. _____

7. A hen can lay eggs. _____

8. A cat has six legs. _____

9. A big bus can jump up and down. _____

10. You can go fast in a jet. _____

11. An ant is as big as an ox. _____

12. Six is less than ten. _____

13. You can rest in a bed. _____

14. You have ten fingers and ten toes. _____

Home Ask your child to circle and read the short e words in each sentence.

Phonics & Spelling

Say and spell each short vowel word. Print the word on the banner of the plane that shows its short vowel sound.

Word List	net	wig	ox	cab	bun
	ram	nut	doll	leg	dish
	lips	web	ax	sun	box

Short a

Short e

Short i

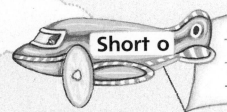

Short o

Short u

Lesson 20

Short vowels a, i, u, o, e: Spelling

45

Phonics & Writing

▶ **Write** a postcard to tell a friend about the fun you had at the beach. **Use** some of your spelling words in your postcard.

dig	fun	swim	hot	camp
run	net	doll	hot sand	pet

TO:
My Friend
2 Blue Lane
Yourtown, USA
12345

Book Corner

A Lot Happened Today
by Judy Nayer

When Jared's teacher gives him a journal, he records his starring role in a baseball game.

Home Ask your child to name the words on the postcard that have short vowel sounds.

1-2nd grade

Pg 35-46

6

When you
tag someone,
he becomes
It and must
keep
his hand on
the spot
you tagged.

8

you
up
...er kind
...that is
play?

TALK
ABOUT IT

— FOLD —

FOLD

3

When you tag someone, she links arms
with you. Then both of you chase the
rest. Everyone you tag joins the chain!

Chain Tag

This book belongs to

1

Twists on Tag

7

Flashlight Tag

Had enough fun in the sun? Play tag in the dark. Just hit someone with a flash of light and yell, "Tag, you're It!"

FOLD

5

Shadow Tag

You need to have sun for this twist on tag. To tag someone, you must step on her shadow!

FOLD

2

Tag is fun to play. But just plain tag can get boring fast. Here are some twists to make the fun of tag last.

4

Rainbow Tag

When you become It, you name a color. You can only tag children who are wearing that color.

Read **each riddle.** Circle **the word that answers the riddle.** Print **it on the line.**

1. This can fly. _____ rake   kite   kit

2. A dog can wag it. _____ tail   tie   pat

3. We did it to a cake. _____ at   time   ate

4. Jane has a can of it. _____ pat   pant   paint

5. We ride boats on this. _____ bat   mile   lake

6. We like to eat it. _____ bit   pie   pat

7. We can ride it. _____ bill   bat   bike

8. We do this to shoes. _____ tip   tie   time

9. We can save this. _____ like   dime   dip

10. A wet day has this. _____ rain   rake   ran

11. We play this. _____ bat   gate   game

12. A clock tells this. _____ time   Tim   take

Read the words in the balloons. **Print** the long **a** words under Kay's name. **Print** the long **i** words under Mike's name.

pan

tail

sail

bake

pat

lid

kite

like

lake

ride

pin

bike

rake

side

cake

dime

Kay

Mike

Lesson 25
Review long vowels a, i

Home

Have your child suggest one or more additional long *a* or long *i* words.

Sue's old blue truck has bells.
It sings some jolly tunes.
Sue loves the way it sounds,
But not its smelly fumes!

▶ **Circle yes or no to answer each sentence. Then circle the long u word in each sentence. Print it on the line.**

> **RULE**
> If a word or syllable has two vowels, the first vowel usually stands for the long sound, and the second vowel is silent. You can hear the long **u** sound in **Sue, blue,** and **fumes**.

1. A red vase is blue. _____ yes no

2. We can get toothpaste in a tube. _____ yes no

3. A baby lion is a cube. _____ yes no

4. A mule has nine tails. _____ yes no

5. You stick things together with glue. _____ yes no

6. We can eat a suit. _____ yes no

7. A rule is a top that can sing. _____ yes no

8. We play a song with a flute. _____ yes no

9. We can hum a tune. _____ yes no

Lesson 26
Long vowel u: Words in context

59

Read the words in the box. Print the short u words in the ducks' pond. Print the long u words in the mule's pen.

bug	jump	suit	tune	bump	tube
dug	glue	nut	rule	use	hum
	luck	jug	blue	flute	

short

long

Lesson 26
Long vowel u

Home

Ask your child to suggest a short *u* name for the duck and a long *u* name for the mule.

Read **each word**. If the word has a long vowel, fill in **the bubble in front of long.** If the word has a short vowel, fill in **the bubble in front of short.**

1 late ○ long ○ short

2 June ○ long ○ short

3 mule ○ long ○ short

4 man ○ long ○ short

5 tube ○ long ○ short

6 ride ○ long ○ short

7 rain ○ long ○ short

8 pick ○ long ○ short

9 six ○ long ○ short

10 use ○ long ○ short

11 cute ○ long ○ short

12 cap ○ long ○ short

13 bat ○ long ○ short

14 time ○ long ○ short

15 fun ○ long ○ short

16 bake ○ long ○ short

17 lick ○ long ○ short

18 us ○ long ○ short

19 map ○ long ○ short

20 wide ○ long ○ short

21 gate ○ long ○ short

22 wipe ○ long ○ short

23 pie ○ long ○ short

24 tune ○ long ○ short

Circle the word that will finish each sentence. **Print** it on the line.

1. We _____ to play music.   ride   like   hike

2. It is a nice _____ to spend a day.   pay   side   way

3. June likes to play her _____.   flute   suit   time

4. Jay can play his _____.   bake   tuba   tub

5. Mike _____ tunes on his bugle.   side   skit   plays

6. Sue plays a _____, too.   bugle   suit   like

7. _____ like to play my drum.   It   I   Ice

8. We all sing _____.   tunes   times   tiles

9. We can play _____ in a parade.   music   suit   fan

10. Will our uniforms come on _____?   tip   cub   time

11. We play at a football _____, too!   gum   game   gate

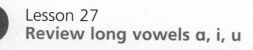 **What kind of group do the children belong to?**

Home

Ask your child to group the words he or she wrote according to the vowel sound.

 **Phonics & Reading**

Read the story. **Print** a long **a**, **i**, or **u** word from the story on the line to finish each sentence.

Playing for the President

Julie plays the tuba in her school band. Her friend Dave plays the flute. They are very excited. They are going to the White House to play for the President.

Washington, D.C. is far away from home so they take the train. They spend the time playing games. The next day they arrive at the station.

At the White House everyone waits. When the President comes out, Julie takes a deep breath and begins to play. The President smiles. He likes their music. When he leaves he hums a tune.

1. The band rides in a _____ to Washington, D.C.

2. Julie plays the _____, and Dave plays the _____.

3. The President _____ their _____.

 **How do you know it was a long train ride?**

Phonics & Writing

Write about a trip you have taken with your class. Where did you go? How did you get there? What did you see? Use some of the words in the box.

train	bike	sail	blue
use	away	lake	hike
time	like	ride	day

Lesson 28
Review long a, i, u: Writing

Home

Ask your child to spell the words in the box.

I know a silly mole
in a yellow overcoat.
He rows down the coast
in a little silver boat.

I hope to go with Mole
to places near and far.
If we can't go by boat,
then we'll go by car.

RULE

If a word or syllable has two vowels, the first vowel usually stands for the long sound, and the second vowel is silent. You can hear the long **o** sound in **know, mole,** and **boat.**

▶ **Find the word in the box that will finish each sentence. Print it on the line.**

coat
owner
Rover
show
bowl
bone
nose

1. Rover poked his _____ into his bowl.

2. He hoped to find a _____.

3. There was no bone in his _____.

4. Then along came his _____, Joe.

5. Something was in the pocket of Joe's _____.

6. Joe said, "I have something to _____ you."

7. Oh, boy! It was a bone for _____.

 **THINK!** **What do dogs like to do with bones?**

Lesson 29
Long vowel o: Words in context

65

Circle the name of each picture.

1

cot   coat

2

road   rod

3

got   goat

4

note   not

5

sap   soap

6

rope   rot

Say the word in the box. Then read the sentence. To finish the sentence, think of a word that rhymes with the word in the box. Print the word on the line.

7. Joe was taking a ride in his _____.

8. Joe's dog Rover wanted to _____, too.

9. Rover poked Joe with his _____.

10. Joe told Rover to _____ into the boat.

11. Then Joe untied the _____.

12. Finally, Joe began to _____.

coat
no
rose
top
hope
bow

Lesson 29
Review long vowel o

Ask your child to spell the words he or she wrote.

▶ **Print** the name of each picture on the line.

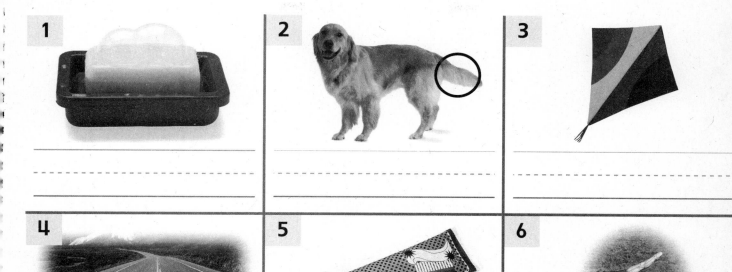

1	2	3

4	5	6

▶ **What would you pack if you were taking a trip? Choose a word from the suitcase that rhymes and print it on the line.**

7. Very nice! Pack some toy _____.

8. Oh, my! Don't forget your _____.

9. How cute! Take your bathing _____.

10. For goodness' sake! Bring a little _____.

tie
mice
suit
rake

Lesson 30
Review long vowels a, i, u, o

67

Fill in the bubble in front of the word that will finish each sentence. Print the word on the line.

1. Tim had a nice _____ outside. ○ Tim ○ time

2. He _____ his bike. ○ rode ○ rod

3. He flew his _____ with June. ○ kite ○ kit

4. He played _____ and seek. ○ hid ○ hide

5. Then _____ and June came inside. ○ Tim ○ time

6. They _____ some cookies. ○ mad ○ made

7. They _____ every single bite. ○ ate ○ at

8. "Let's make ice _____," said June. ○ cubes ○ cub

9. "We can _____ grape juice." ○ us ○ use

10. Next Tim made a paper _____. ○ plan ○ plane

11. June made a paper _____. ○ hate ○ hat

12. Tim said, "I _____ you had fun." ○ hope ○ hop

THINK! Do you think Tim and June had fun? Why or why not?

Lesson 30
Review long vowels a, i, u, o

Home

Ask your child to read the sentences and identify which words have long vowel sounds.

How many pairs of sneakers does an airplane need?

- Enough for twenty thousand feet.

▶ Circle **the name of each picture.**

1	set / seal / seed	**2**	feel / fell / feet	**3**	jays / jeans / jeeps
4	bet / bee / beat	**5**	beets / beds / beads	**6**	jet / jeep / Jean

▶ Circle **the word that will finish each sentence.** Underline **the letters that stand for the long e sound.** Then print **the word on the line.**

7. Seals live in the _____.   seat   sea   set

8. They _____ fish.   neat   eat   feet

9. We can teach _____ tricks.   east   seals   beets

10. Have you _____ a seal show?   set   free   seen

11. We will see one next _____.   week   met   beak

Circle the long e words in the puzzle.

k	f	s	r	j
s	e	e	n	e
a	e	a	o	a
s	t	t	p	n
p	e	a	b	s

jeans

feet

pea

seat

seen

Write the word from the box that will finish each sentence.

1. I wore my new blue _____ to the zoo.

2. I sat on a _____ that had gum on it.

3. I spilled _____ soup on my jeans.

4. Mud from my _____ splashed on them.

5. I've never _____ such a big mess.

Home   Ask your child to read the answers and tell what letters stand for the long e sound.

Say the name of each picture. Print the vowel you hear on the first line. If the vowel is short, print an **S** on the second line. If the vowel is long, print an **L** on the second line.

1	2	3	4

5	6	7	8

9	10	11	12

Finish the rhyming words.

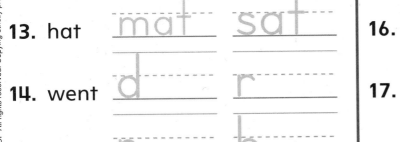

13. hat   mat   sat

14. went   d   r

15. fun   r   b

16. gate   l   d

17. like   b   h

18. goat   c   b

1. boat _____

2. sod _____

3. red _____

4. oar _____

5. hop _____

6. ran _____

7. cone _____

8. wide _____

9. bake _____

10. nip _____

11. tame _____

12. map _____

Find a word in the box that rhymes with each word. **Print** it on the line.

13. time _____

14. cube _____

15. rub _____

16. need _____

17. tape _____

18. bat _____

19. clue _____

| tube |
| cub |
| blue |
| cape |
| dime |
| hat |
| feed |

20. seat _____

21. fin _____

22. hope _____

23. bet _____

24. rob _____

25. toad _____

26. fine _____

| tin |
| road |
| cob |
| mine |
| rope |
| get |
| heat |

Lesson 32
Review long and short vowels

Home

Ask your child to read the rhyming words and tell whether each pair has a long or short vowel sound.

 **Phonics & Spelling**

Say and spell each long vowel word. Print the word on the train that shows its long vowel sound.

Word List

use	heel	hay	nine	note
coat	tube	dime	rule	bead
cape	tie	seen	mail	row

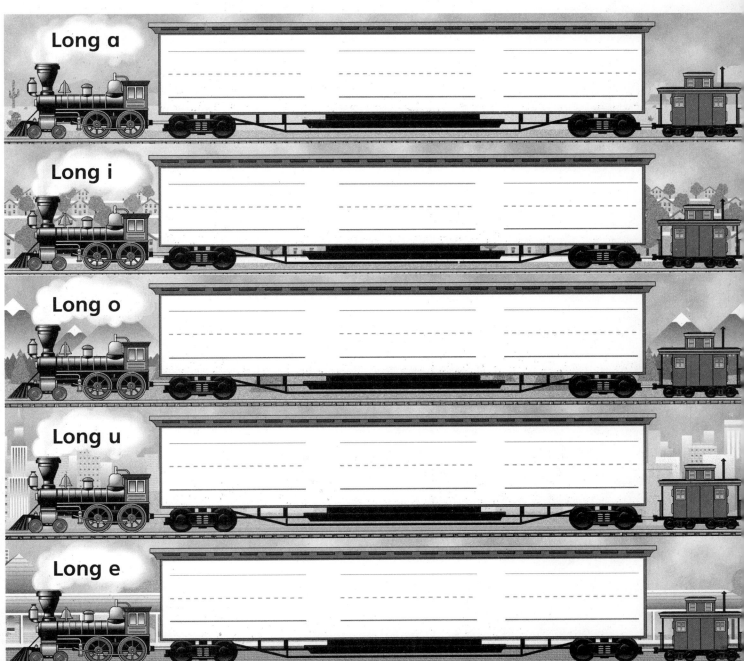

Long a

Long i

Long o

Long u

Long e

Phonics & Writing

▶ **Write about a place you have visited or would like to visit. Use some of the words in the box.**

blue	boat	hay	hole	seat
mail	jeans	hope	train	row
bike	ride	use	time	rain

Book Corner

Summer at Cove Lake
by Judy Lechner

A young girl finds many new things when she spends the summer with her aunt.

Home Help your child think of a title for his or her story.

6

Do you like animals? Then the San Diego Zoo in California is the place for you.

8

TALK ABOUT IT

What special place would you like to see? How would you get there?

FOLD

FOLD

3

Climb up high. You can see the whole city. Everything looks tiny from way up here.

So Many Sights to See

This book belongs to:

1

Review long vowels: Take-Home Book

7

Take the zoo train to see the lions, tigers, zebras, and apes. Don't forget the seals!

5

From the plane you can see people riding mules down a steep path.

FOLD

FOLD

There are so many exciting places to see. You can take a boat to the Statue of Liberty in New York.

2

You can fly over the Grand Canyon in Arizona. It is very wide and very deep.

4

Say the name of each picture. Print the vowel you hear on the line. Then circle the word short if the vowel is short. Circle the word long if it is long.

1
_____ long
_____ short

2
_____ long
_____ short

3
_____ long
_____ short

4
_____ long
_____ short

5
_____ long
_____ short

6
_____ long
_____ short

7
_____ long
_____ short

8
_____ long
_____ short

9
_____ long
_____ short

10
_____ long
_____ short

11
_____ long
_____ short

12
_____ long
_____ short

13
_____ long
_____ short

14
_____ long
_____ short

15
_____ long
_____ short

16
_____ long
_____ short

Fill in the bubble in front of the word that will finish each sentence.

1. I have a ___ named Wags.   ○ fog   ○ dog   ○ day

2. His ___ always wags.   ○ tap   ○ tape   ○ tail

3. Wags is a very ___ dog.   ○ cute   ○ cut   ○ cat

4. He ___ food by the bags.   ○ eats   ○ ears   ○ east

5. His tummy is ___ and sags.   ○ bite   ○ big   ○ kite

6. His long ears flap ___ flags.   ○ like   ○ lime   ○ lit

7. Wags and I like to ___.   ○ fat   ○ way   ○ play

8. We like to ___ walks, too.   ○ take   ○ tack   ○ tail

9. I ___ him to go one way.   ○ fell   ○ tell   ○ bean

10. He always ___ the other way.   ○ toes   ○ got   ○ goes

11. But he would never ___ away.   ○ fun   ○ run   ○ use

12. A dog like Wags is a ___ of fun.   ○ lot   ○ lock   ○ low

▶ **What is wrong with this picture?**

THINK! **What do you think a scarecrow does in the garden?**

Home Letter

Dear Family,

In the next few weeks we'll be learning about different kinds of words and sounds: compounds (scarecrow), consonant blends (grapes), digraphs (peach, wheat), r-controlled vowels (corn), and y as a vowel (cherry). We will also be learning about nature and the world outside.

| scarecrow | grapes | peach | wheat | corn | cherry |

At-Home Activities

Here are some activities you and your child can do together.

▶ Plant a bean or some grass seed in a paper cup. Talk about what seeds need to grow.

▶ Write the following words on separate pieces of paper: sail, boat, pop, corn, mail, box, note, and book. Take turns pairing the words to make compound words. Make a list of compound words with your child and add to it as you think of new words.

Book Corner

You and your child might enjoy reading these books together.

Potato
by Barrie Watts

Children learn about potato plants and how edible parts grow underground.

Alphabet Garden
by Laura Jane Coats

Children take an alphabetical tour of a garden.

Sincerely,

Name _____

Granddad planted something for me.
He said, "It's called a dogwood tree.
Of course it cannot bark or bite!
In the springtime it will be pink or white."

▶ Say the words in each box. Put two words together to make new words. Print the new words on the lines.

RULE

A **compound word** is made up of two or more words joined together to make a new word. **Granddad** is made from the words **grand** and **dad.**

1	pea weed
	sea nut

peanut

_____

_____

2	meal oat
	my self

_____

_____

3	cup rain
	coat cake

_____

_____

4	be rail
	road may

_____

_____

5	base class
	mate ball

_____

_____

6	pack corn
	back pop

_____

_____

Look at the picture. **Read** the two words below it. **Put** them together to make one new word that names the picture. **Print** the new word on the line to finish the sentence.

1.   mail + box   A box for mail is a _____.

2.   rain + coat   A coat for rain is a _____.

3.   back + pack   A pack for your back is a _____.

4.   sail + boat   A boat with a sail is a _____.

5.   pop + corn   Corn that can pop is _____.

6.   sand + box   A box full of sand is a _____.

7.   cup + cake   A cake in a cup is a _____.

Home   Help your child think of other compound words and draw pictures of each one.

Name _____

Farmer Janet picks some carrots.
She picks a turnip, too.
She'll take these to her cabin
And make a farmer's stew.

 Say the name of each picture. **Circle** each vowel you hear. **Print** the number of syllables you hear on the line.

Many words are made of small parts called syllables. Each syllable has one vowel sound.
p(i)cks = 1 syllable   c(a)rr(o)ts = 2 syllables

1	basket
2	mittens
3	steps
4	pencil
5	tent
6	puppet
7	trunk
8	robot
9	pillow
10	kitten
11	tray
12	lemon

Find the word in the box that names each picture. **Print** it on the line to finish the sentence.

ribbon	basket	button	pillow
kitten	boxes	seven	baby

1. Molly got a _____ named Popcorn.

2. She put a _____ in Popcorn's fur.

3. Popcorn was only _____ weeks old.

4. She had a nose like a _____.

5. She liked to play inside _____.

6. Molly made a bed for Popcorn in a _____.

7. She put a _____ in the bed to make it soft.

8. Popcorn was like a little _____.

 **Why is Popcorn like a baby?**

Lesson 37
Two-syllable words: Words in context

 Say one- and two-syllable words and have your child identify the number of syllables.

Name _____

Pick a bag of apples.
Pick a basket of cucumbers, too.
There's some applesauce
on the table,
And a dill pickle just for you.

▶ Find **the** name of each picture in the box. **Print** it on the line.

apple	eagle	people
candle	buckle	whistle
turtle	bottle	table

1 _____

2 _____

3 _____

4 _____

5 _____

6 _____

7 _____

8 _____

9 _____

Lesson 38

85

Words ending in le: Picture-text match

1. A _____ uses its own shell for a house.

2. It can swim in a small _____.

3. It can _____ around in the puddle.

4. It climbs on rocks and _____.

5. An _____ might fly over and scare it.

6. Sometimes, _____ may scare it, too.

7. Then the turtle can _____ safely in its shell.

pebbles
eagle
people
turtle
huddle
puddle
paddle

8. I have a _____ pet turtle.

9. My _____ gave it to me.

10. It's not even as big as a _____.

11. I named my turtle _____.

12. When I hold it, its feet _____ my hand.

13. Then I laugh and _____.

14. Sometimes, it sits on the _____ next to my bed.

giggle
table
little
Wiggle
pickle
tickle
uncle

 **Where do the two turtles in the story live?**

 Home Help your child make up sentences using some of the words in the boxes.

Mice can come to this place.
It's such a nice place to race.
They climb in and peek out of the spaces.
Then they stop and wash their faces!

 Say the name of each picture. If it has a soft **c** sound, circle the picture. If it has a hard **c** sound, draw a line under it.

RULE

When **c** is followed by **e, i,** or **y,** it usually has a soft sound. You can hear the soft **c** sound in **mice.**

1 face	**2** cap	**3** clock
4 cup	**5** pencil	**6** cake
7 mice	**8** ice	**9** celery

Lesson 39
Hard and soft c: Phonemic awareness

87

Circle the word that will finish each sentence. **Print** it on the line.

1. Cindy and Vince _____ run fast.

| can | cage |
| cape | came |

2. They will run in a _____.

| mice | race |
| nice | next |

3. The kids _____ to watch.

| cap | cane |
| come | cat |

4. Cindy hopes to win first _____.

| nice | rice |
| place | slice |

5. The _____ of their shoes are tied.

| rice | nice |
| laces | price |

6. They race to the _____.

| next | nice |
| fence | celery |

7. It's a tie. They both win _____ prizes.

| mice | cereal |
| nice | price |

8. Cindy and Vince have smiling _____.

| lace | faces |
| race | space |

9. The kids buy ice-cream _____.

| cones | cape |
| mice | nice |

10. Vince _____ wait until the next race.

| race | case |
| can't | nice |

 **THINK!** Do Cindy and Vince enjoy racing? How do you know?

Lesson 39
Hard and soft c: Words in context

 Home Help your child group all the hard c words, and then all the soft c words.

Name _____

Gentle giraffes,
Gaze through the trees.
Bigger than giants,
They nibble the leaves.

Say the name of each picture. If the name has a soft **g** sound, **circle** the picture. If it has a hard **g** sound, **draw a line** under it.

1

game

2

gym

3

goat

4

page

5

giant

6
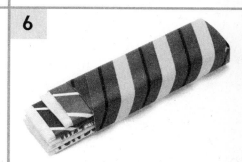
gum

7

dragon

8

egg

9

giraffe

> The letter **g** can make a hard or a soft sound. **Read the words in the box. Listen** for the sounds of **g**. **Print** the words under Soft **g** or Hard **g**.

gift	gem	age	dog	cage	large	good	gum
huge	gave	goat	stage	wag	page	wage	gold
gym	gate	giant	gentle	egg	game	giraffe	give

Soft g Words

_____

_____

_____

_____

_____

_____

_____

_____

_____

Hard g Words

_____

_____

_____

_____

_____

_____

_____

_____

_____

Lesson 40
Hard and soft g

Say a word from the box. Ask your child to spell it and tell if the word has a soft or hard *g* sound.

Name _____

▶ Read the words in the box. Draw a green line under each word that has a hard **c** or **g** sound. Print each word that has a soft **c** or **g** sound on a line.

giant
price
mice
goat
age
wage
games
huge
cent
ice
gym
cake
race
rice
gas
cone
face

_____ _____

_____ _____

_____ _____

_____ _____

_____ _____

Hard and soft c, g

Read each word. Print s beside each word with a soft c or g sound. Print h beside each word with a hard c or g sound.

1. nice ___   2. cuff ___   3. ice ___

4. cabin ___   5. lunge ___   6. camel ___

7. game ___   8. race ___   9. gull ___

10. age ___   11. came ___   12. coast ___

13. cake ___   14. coat ___   15. pencil ___

16. gym ___   17. cent ___   18. giant ___

19. gate ___   20. ridge ___   21. care ___

22. goes ___   23. recess ___   24. Vince ___

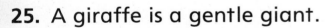 **Draw a red box around each word with a soft g sound. Draw a blue circle around each word with a soft c sound.**

25. A giraffe is a gentle giant.

26. You can tell by its kind face.

27. A giraffe is taller than most ceilings.

28. Giraffes think large leaves are delicious.

29. Cereal and vegetables make nice giraffe treats.

30. Zoos with giraffes need tall fences.

31. It costs money to go to the zoo in the city.

32. I need to save fifty cents more to go to the zoo.

92 Lesson 41
Hard c and soft g

 Help your child group the words at the top of the page into four lists: hard c, soft c, hard g, and soft g.

Name _____

**Phonics &
Reading**

▶ **Read** the story. **Print** a word from the story to finish each sentence.

JACK and the MAGIC BEANSTALK

Jack had a magic bean. He planted it in his backyard. The next day he found a huge beanstalk. "Maybe I can climb it," Jack said.

Jack hoped to find a giant at the top with a bag of gold. But Jack got a big surprise! His mother was sitting there at a table.

"You forgot to eat breakfast," she said.

"Sorry, Mom," Jack said.

She gave Jack a plate of pancakes. He drank a cup of milk and ate an apple. Then she sent him home to wash his face.

1. Jack climbed a huge _____.

2. He wanted to find a _____

   and a bag of _____.

3. Jack drank a _____ of milk and

   ate an _____.

4. He went home to wash his _____.

THINK! How do you know the bean that Jack had was magical?

Lesson 42

93

Compounds; syllables; le; sounds of c, g: Reading

Phonics & Writing

▶ **Jack shared one of his magic beans with you.**
Write a story about what grows in your garden.
Use some of the words in the box.

magic	huge	garden	giggle	people
basket	celery	outdoors	corn	maybe

94

Lesson 42
Compounds; syllables; words with le;
sounds of c, g: Writing

Home

Have your child read the story on
page 93 and identify the
compound and two-syllable words.

Name _____

Green frogs, tree frogs,
There are so many kinds.
Brown frogs, bullfrogs,
We can't make up our minds.

Say the name of each picture. **Print its beginning blend on the line. Trace the whole word.**

RULE

A **consonant blend** is two or more consonants that come together in a word. Their sounds blend together, but each sound is heard. You can hear **r** blends in **green, tree,** and **frogs.**

1

_____apes

2

_____og

3

_____ee

4

_____ain

Use the words above to answer the riddles.

5 I can jump and hop.
You find me in a pond.
I eat bugs.

I am a _____.

6 I am green.
You can find me in a park.
Birds live in me.

I am a _____.

7 I can be small or big.
I make a good toy.
I run on a track.

I am a _____.

8 We grow on vines.
We come in bunches.
We are good to eat.

We are _____.

1

grapes
grass
grade

2

trim
truck
train

3

trade
trap
tree

4

drive
drum
drink

5

from
frost
fruit

6

train
truck
trick

7

dress
drapes
drum

8

gray
grass
grab

► Find **the blend in each word. Circle it. Print it on the line.**

9. b r i n g ____

10. f r y ____

11. t r i p ____

12. g r a d e ____

13. d r i v e ____

14. g r a s s ____

15. b r a v e ____

16. t r i c k ____

17. g r a i n ____

18. b r i d e ____

19. c r u m b ____

20. t r a i n ____

21. c r o s s ____

22. b r i c k ____

23. t r a d e ____

24. f r e e ____

25. p r i c e ____

26. f r u i t ____

Home Ask your child to name the pictures with the same beginning sounds.

The wind blows the clouds.
Sleet turns to snow.
Winter's here again,
And sledding we will go!

▶ **Say** the name of each picture. **Print** its beginning blend on the line.

1		2		3	
_____		_____		_____	
4		5		6	
_____		_____		_____	

▶ **Circle** the word that will finish each sentence. **Print** it on the line.

7. Snow covers the ground like a white

_____.   cloud   clap

8. The wind _____ the snow around.   blue   blows

9. It covers the trees and _____, too.   plants   plays

10. I like to _____ in the snow.   play   plants

11. I am _____ that it's wintertime.   glad   glass

Print the word on the line that answers each riddle. The pictures will help you.

1 Sometimes I ring. Sometimes I chime. I tick-tock all the time.

_____

2 High up on a pole I go. With the wind I flap and blow.

_____

3 I hold your food. Look for me under your hot dog.

_____

4 I make things stick for you. I stick to you, too.

_____

Find a word in the box to finish each sentence. Print it on the line.

5. I have a new magnifying _____.

6. When I hold it _____ to things, they get bigger.

7. A blade of _____ looks like a tree trunk.

8. _____ of wood are really full of holes.

9. A _____ looks like a big black monster!

10. A toy _____ looks like a real plane.

Blocks
grass
fly
plane
close
glass

Lesson 44
Blends with l

Home   Ask your child to name other words that begin with cl, fl, pl, and bl.

Name _____

> Write the name of each picture. Then find the words in the puzzle and circle them. Look for words that go across and down.

1 _____

2 _____

3 _____

4 _____

5 _____

6 _____

7 _____

8 _____

9 _____

10 _____

11 _____

12 _____

```
a  x  g  r  a  s  s  t  c  p
m  s  l  i  p  p  e  r  s  l
c  l  o  u  d  n  t  u  g  a
f  f  b  r  e  a  d  c  l  n
r  l  e  b  r  i  c  k  a  t
o  a  x  t  r  e  e  m  s  w
g  g  q  l  p  u  y  y  s  u
```

Lesson 45
Review blends with r and l

99

Print the name of each picture on the line.

1	2	3	4

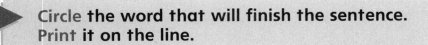

_____   _____   _____   _____

**Circle the word that will finish the sentence.
Print it on the line.**

5. Every day a _____ comes
   to my window.   from   crow   trim

6. It is big and _____.   play   drink   black

7. I am always _____
   to see my crow.   grade   glad   glass

8. It likes to get a _____
   from our sprinkler.   drum   dress   drink

9. Some days I fix it a _____
   of crumbs.   plate   play   plum

10. Crows like to eat bugs

    in the _____.   grass   grab   grape

11. They eat bugs in _____, too.   train   trees   truck

Take turns with your child naming
other words with _r_ and _l_ blends.

Name _____

Said Squiggle Snake to Slimy Snail,
"Let's slide on the slippery wet grass."
Said Slimy Snail to Squiggle Snake,
"Slow down! You move too fast!"

> Say the name of each picture. Find its beginning blend in the box. Print it on the line.

| sc | st | sp | sn | squ | scr | str | sl | sm | sw |

1

_____

2

_____

3

_____

4

_____

5

_____

6

_____

7

_____

8

_____

9

_____

10

_____

11

_____

12

_____

Lesson 46
Blends with s: Phonemic awareness

101

▶ **Find a word in the box to finish each sentence. Print it on the line.**

1. Did you ever _____ to think about snakes?

2. Snakes have long, _____ bodies.

3. Snakes can move both fast and _____.

4. _____ have no arms or legs.

5. They still have the _____ to move.

6. Snakes can even _____.

7. Their _____ looks slimy, but it's dry.

8. Snakes _____ some people, but not me.

scare
slim
skin
stop
skill
Snakes
swim
slow

▶ **Circle the name of each picture.**

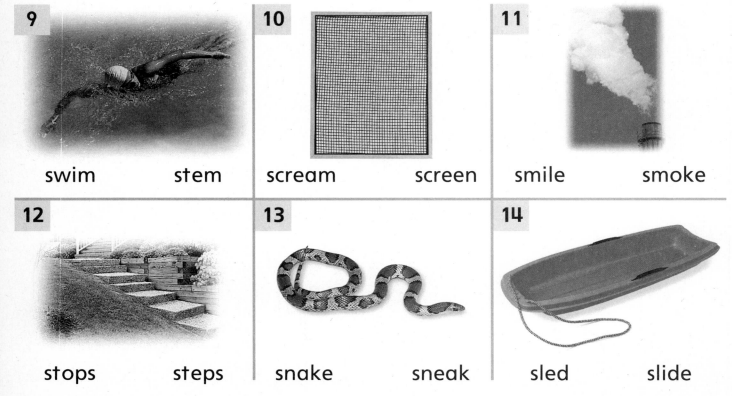

9	10	11
swim stem	scream screen	smile smoke

12	13	14
stops steps	snake sneak	sled slide

Help your child identify the words in the box that have the same beginning sound.

Name _____

My swing is next to the tree trunk.
My tree fort is near the trunk, too.
Best of all, there's a hole for the chipmunk!
What's left for this tree trunk to do?

Remember that in a **consonant blend** the sounds of the consonants blend together, but each sound is heard. You can hear blends at the end of **swing** and **trunk.**

▶ Circle **the word that answers each riddle. Print it on the line.**

1 All mail needs these. What are they? stamps stumps _____	**2** We can ride on it. What is it? string swing _____	**3** An elephant has one. What is it? skunk trunk _____
4 We can eat it. What is it? toast list _____	**5** It hides your face. What is it? task mask _____	**6** We can sleep in it. What is it? tent plant _____
7 We have two of these. What are they? lands hands _____	**8** Fish swim in it. What is it? tank wink _____	**9** It can float. What is it? raft left _____

Find the word in the box that names each picture.
Print it on the line.

milk	skunk	tent	belt	trunk	plants
nest	ring	stamp	raft	desk	mask

1
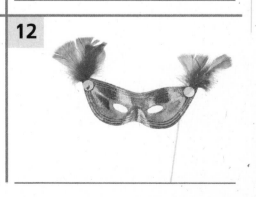
_____

2

_____

3

_____

4

_____

5

_____

6

_____

7

_____

8

_____

9

_____

10

_____

11

_____

12

_____

Lesson 47
Final blends: Picture-text match

Home

Ask your child to name other words
that end with *ng, sk,* and *mp.*

Name _____

▶ **Read** the story. **Use** a word from the story to finish each sentence. **Print** the word on the line.

SUNFLOWERS

Wild sunflowers first grew on the plains in the West. Native Americans roasted the seeds and ground them into flour for bread. We still eat sunflower seeds. They are a great food for birds and people.

Spanish explorers brought sunflower plants back to Europe. Now sunflowers grow all over the world. Sunflowers grow in many different sizes. The smallest are only one or two feet tall. The biggest plants are twelve feet tall!

1. Sunflowers first grew on the _____.

2. People ground the seeds into _____.

3. Then they used the flour to make _____.

4. _____ explorers brought sunflowers to Europe.

THINK! **Why did Spanish explorers bring sunflowers to Europe?**

Phonics &
Writing

flowers
plants
green
glad
fruit
grow
best
trees
grapes
want

_____

_____

_____

_____

_____

_____

_____

_____

Home Ask your child to read his or her description. Guess the name of the plant.

Name _____

Baby bird, baby bird, are you ready?
Baby bird, baby bird, can you try?
Spread your tiny, feathery wings,
For now it is time to fly!

RULE

Sometimes **y** can stand for the vowel sound of long **e** or long **i**. You can hear the long **e** sound in **baby**.

▶ Circle **each word in which y has a long e sound.**

1. baby
2. cry
3. happy
4. why

5. try
6. every
7. hurry
8. tiny

9. Molly
10. sandy
11. shy
12. puppy

13. penny
14. Freddy
15. funny
16. bunny

▶ Circle **the words in the sentences in which y has a long e sound.**

17. Ty and Molly were helping take care of baby Freddy.

18. They heard Freddy cry in his crib.

19. They went to help in a hurry.

20. They had to try everything to make him happy.

21. Ty read him a funny book about fish that fly.

22. Molly gave him her bunny to play with.

23. Ty made very silly faces.

24. Finally, Freddy was happy.

Circle **each word with a y that sounds like long i.**

1. try	2. Freddy	3. sly	4. buggy	5. funny
6. bunny	7. dry	8. silly	9. rocky	10. my
11. Ty	12. windy	13. by	14. sky	15. sunny
16. sleepy	17. fly	18. happy	19. muddy	20. cry
21. sneaky	22. lucky	23. shy	24. puppy	25. Molly
26. why	27. jolly	28. baby	29. fry	30. very

Circle **each word with y that sounds like long i in the sentences.**

31. Why do onions make us cry when we are happy ?

32. Why is the sky blue on a sunny day ?

33. Why do bats fly at night ?

34. Why is a desert dry and a swamp muddy ?

35. Why can a bird fly but not a puppy ?

36. Why do we look silly if we try to fly ?

37. Why is a fox sneaky and sly ?

38. Why is a bunny shy ?

39. Why does a rainy sky make you sleepy ?

40. Do you ever wonder why ?

Home

Ask your child to use three of the circled words on this page in a sentence.

Name _____

> **Read the word in each paw print. If the y stands for a long i sound, draw a line under the word. If it stands for a long e sound, circle the word.**

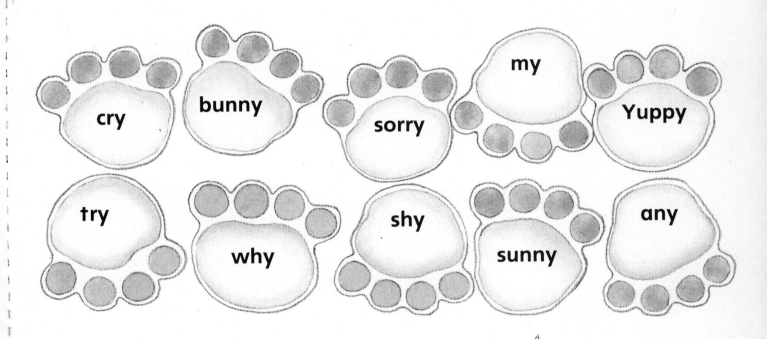

cry   bunny   sorry   my   Yuppy

try   why   shy   sunny   any

> **Find a word from the top of the page to finish each sentence. Print it on the line.**

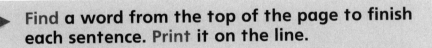

1. _____ the puppy was digging a hole.

2. Suddenly he heard a _____ from inside.

3. A very angry _____ popped out of the hole.

4. "Why are you digging up _____ happy home?"

5. Yuppy yapped, "Oh, my! I'm very _____."

6. "I'll _____ to help you fix it up!"

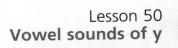

Lesson 50
Vowel sounds of y   109

Say the name of each picture. Circle each word
that has the same sound of **y** as the picture name.

1

baby
my
fly
fifty
funny

2

sky
sunny
fairy
cry
Bobby

3

dolly
try
sly
kitty
dry

4

lady
penny
shy
fry
happy

5

why
silly
lily
by
bunny

6

my
sixty
fly
Sally
sky

7

jelly
Sandy
my
fry
cry

8

lucky
try
fifty
sky
puppy

9

berry
very
try
sly
any

10

cry
lady
many
sky
by

11

only
city
July
spy
funny

12

my
fly
fifty
happy
silly

110

Lesson 50
Vowel sounds of y

Help your child find two words that
rhyme in each box.

Name _____

Phonics & Spelling

Say the name of each picture. Find the word inside the grasshopper and spell it. Then print the word on the line.

1 	2 	3 	4 
_____	_____	_____	_____

5 	6 	7 	8 
_____	_____	_____	_____

9 	10 	11 	12 
_____	_____	_____	_____

Word List

ribbon	gym	globe	baby
stamp	peanut	apple	sky
plant	belt	ice	frog

Compounds; syllables; le; hard and soft c, g; blends; vowel y: Spelling

▶ Write a story about a grasshopper in a garden. Use some of the words below. Read your story to a friend.

grasshopper	trees	gloves	plants	grow
flowers	smile	glad	fruit	grapes
scarecrow	just	must	best	green

Lesson 51
Compounds; syllables; le; hard and soft c, g; blends; vowel y: Writing

 Home Ask your child to read his or her story to you.

Johnny Appleseed

This book belongs to:

1

FOLD

Johnny Appleseed wanted people to have juicy fruit to eat. So he cleared the land and planted apple trees.

3

FOLD

TALK ABOUT IT

Why do you think Johnny Appleseed wanted to plant apple trees?

8

Johnny Appleseed was a friend to Native Americans. No animals ever harmed him.

6

Lesson 52

113

Compounds; syllables; le; hard and soft c, g; blends; vowel y: Take-Home Book

4

Johnny Appleseed walked through Ohio, Indiana, and Illinois. He carried bags of seeds with him. He made many trips.

ILLINOIS

INDIANA

OHIO

2

John Chapman was born in 1774 in Massachusetts. You might know him better as Johnny Appleseed.

FOLD

FOLD

Some people thought Johnny Appleseed was a little odd. He walked barefoot. He often gave away the money that people gave him.

5

For forty years he tramped all over the country. Everywhere he went, he planted apple orchards.

7

Compounds; syllables; le; hard and soft c, g; blends; vowel y: Take-Home Book

Name _____

Shiny wet shells on the shore,
More shells down the beach,
There's such a lot to choose from!
Why don't we pick one of each?

▶ Circle **the word that will finish each sentence. Print it on the line.**

1. I go to the zoo to see the _____.   chop   chimp   check

2. It smiles to show its _____.   then   teeth   these

3. They are big and _____.   which   what   white

4. It eats bananas by the _____.   bunch   reach   much

5. Once I saw it eat a _____.   that   ship   peach

6. Sometimes it dumps its _____.   wish   dish   swish

7. Then it naps in the _____.   fresh   shut   shade

▶ Find **two words from the list above that begin with ch, wh, th, and sh. Print them on the lines beside the correct consonant digraph.**

8		9	
ch	_____	th	_____
	_____		_____

10		11	
wh	_____	sh	_____
	_____		_____

Fill in the bubble beside the word that will finish each sentence. Print it on the line.

1. Chip and I didn't know ——————— to go.
   - ⃝ where
   - ⃝ what

2. We decided to go to the mall to ———————.
   - ⃝ chop
   - ⃝ shop

3. They sell everything ———————.
   - ⃝ this
   - ⃝ there

4. There was so ———————to choose from.
   - ⃝ catch
   - ⃝ much

5. I couldn't decide ——————— I wanted most.
   - ⃝ what
   - ⃝ who

6. Then I saw some model ——————— kits.
   - ⃝ shirt
   - ⃝ ship

7. ——————— was what I wanted most.
   - ⃝ When
   - ⃝ That

8. I ——————— a clipper ship to make.
   - ⃝ chose
   - ⃝ chair

9. ——————— chose a spaceship kit.
   - ⃝ Choose
   - ⃝ Chip

10. ——————— we had lunch.
    - ⃝ Then
    - ⃝ That

THINK! Where do you think Chip bought his model kit?

Lesson 53
Consonant digraphs sh, th, wh, ch

Home

Say one of the words in the list. Have your child name the other words that begin with the same sound.

Name _____

1
th
sh
ck
ch
wh

2
th
sh
ck
ch
wh

3
th
sh
ck
ch
wh

4
th
sh
ck
ch
wh

5
th
sh
ck
ch
wh

6
th
sh
ck
ch
wh

7
th
sh
ck
ch
wh

8
th
sh
ck
ch
wh

9
th
sh
ck
ch
wh

10
th
sh
ck
ch
wh

11
th
sh
ck
ch
wh

12
th
sh
ck
ch
wh

13
th
sh
ck
ch
wh

14
th
sh
ck
ch
wh

15
th
sh
ck
ch
wh

16
th
sh
ck
ch
wh

Read the words in the box and **circle** the hidden pictures. **Write** the words on the lines. **Circle** the consonant digraph in each word.

whale	wheel	thumb	clock	truck	duck
fish	peach	chair	thimble	shell	shoe

1. _____

2. _____

3. _____

4. _____

5. _____

6. _____

7. _____

8. _____

9. _____

10. _____

11. _____

12. _____

Lesson 54
Review digraphs sh, th, wh, ch, ck

Home

Have your child find the words with the same initial digraphs.

Name _____

We work in our garden.
We get down on our knees.
We kneel to plant flowers.
We kneel to pull weeds.

▶ Read **each sentence. Find** the picture it tells **about. Write the sentence letter under the picture.**

1

a. John has a knot in the rope.
b. I know what is in the box.
c. Joan turned the knob.

_____   _____

2

a. Theo will knock down the pile.
b. Mom cut it with a knife.
c. She knocks on the door.

_____   _____

3

a. The knight wore armor.
b. Tad's knee needs a patch.
c. Grandma likes to knit.

_____   _____

▶ **Find a word in the box that answers each riddle. Print it on the line.**

4. Something that can cut _____

5. Someone who wore armor _____

6. Something you can tie _____

knife
knot
knight

1. I _____ how to do many things.   know   knot

2. I can spread butter with a _____.   knot   knife

3. I can touch my _____ to my chin.   knees   knew

4. I can tie _____.   knots   knits

5. I can turn the _____ of a door.   knee   knob

6. I can read about _____.   know   knights

7. I can _____ a sweater.   knit   knife

8. I've _____ how to do these things for a long time.   knit   known

► **Think** of a word that begins with **kn** and **rhymes** with each word. **Print** the word on the line.

9.   snow   10.   block   11.   wife

_____   _____   _____

12.   blew   13.   see   14.   hot

_____   _____   _____

15.   own   16.   sit   17.   sob

_____   _____   _____

Ask your child to make up sentences
using the *kn* words on the page.

Name _____

The small earthworm wriggles
And wrenches to stay.
The hungry wren wrestles,
But the worm gets away!

▶ **Find** the word in the box that will finish each sentence. **Print** it on the line.

wren	wreck	wrap	wrestle	write
wrist	wrench	wrecker	wrong	wriggle

1. To move around is to _____.

2. The opposite of **right** is _____.

3. A small bird is a _____.

4. A thing that is ruined is a _____.

5. To hide a gift in paper is to _____ it.

6. When you put a story on paper, you _____.

7. Your _____ holds your hand to your arm.

8. A truck that clears away wrecks is a _____.

9. A kind of tool is a _____.

10. One way to fight is to _____.

Find **a word in the box that answers each riddle.**
Print it on the line.

wren	wrecker	wriggle	wrong	wrist
wrench	wreath	writer	typewriter	wrinkle

1 I am a useful tool.
I can fix things.
What am I?

_____

2 I am the opposite of **right**.
I rhyme with **song**.
What am I?

_____

3 I can fly.
I like to sing.
What am I?

_____

4 I am round and pretty.
You can hang me up.
What am I?

_____

5 I am next to a hand.
I can twist and bend.
What am I?

_____

6 I make letters.
People press my keys.
What am I?

_____

7 I am a big truck.
I tow things away.
What am I?

_____

8 I write stories. They can be
real or make-believe.
What am I?

_____

9 I am a fold in a dress.
I am a crease in a face.
What am I?

_____

10 I am another word for **squirm**.
I rhyme with **giggle**.
What am I?

_____

Lesson 56
Consonant digraph wr

Home

Ask your child to circle the letters *wr*
in each word and say the word.

Name _____

Phonics & Reading

▶ **Read** the story. **Use** a word from the story to finish each sentence. **Print** the word on the line.

Chipmunks

The chipmunk's brown coat with its black-and-white stripes helps it blend in with the rocks and bushes. A chipmunk can sit very still. Then it wriggles its nose and twitches its whiskers.

A chipmunk is a shy animal. A sound it does not know may chase it back into its hole. A chipmunk can move fast.

Chipmunks carry food in their cheek pouches. They store nuts and grain in their dens. Then they know they will not go hungry when winter comes.

1. This story is about _____.

2. A chipmunk is a _____ animal.

3. Its brown coat has black-and- _____ stripes.

4. The chipmunk _____ its nose.

What might scare a chipmunk?

Phonics & Writing

Imagine you are a wildlife watcher. Choose one of the animals pictured below. Write what you know about it. Some of the words below may help you.

| when | shell | wriggle | whiskers | flock |
| know | their | show | bunch | chirp |

Lesson 57
Review digraphs: Writing

Home

Say a word from the list and have your child name another word with the same initial or final sound.

Name _____

So many strawberries to pick,
It's hard to know where to start!
Let's pick the largest ones
And bake them in a tart.

▶ Find **the word in the box that will finish each sentence.** Print **it on the line.**

> **RULE**
> An **r** after a vowel makes the vowel sound different from the usual short or long sound. You can hear the **ar** sound in **hard, start,** and **largest.**

apart	star	hard	part	car
hardly	start	large	jars	

1. I picked out a new model _____ kit.

2. I got two _____ of paint, too.

3. I could hardly wait to _____ on it.

4. I glued it so the car wouldn't fall _____.

5. There were small parts and _____ parts.

6. The tires were _____ to fit, but I did it.

7. I stuck gold _____ stickers on the sides.

8. I could _____ believe it when it was done.

9. The best _____ was showing it to my friends.

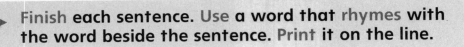

Finish each sentence. Use a word that rhymes with the word beside the sentence. Print it on the line.

1. A shark is a very _____ animal.

2. It lives in the deep, _____ part of the ocean.

3. It can grow to be very _____.

4. A shark's teeth are very _____.

5. It has no problem tearing food _____.

6. I live _____ from the ocean.

7. I like to visit the animal _____.

8. It's not far from my house by _____.

9. I can watch the sharks there free from _____.

part
bark
barge
carp
start
star
lark
tar
farm

Print three rhyming words under each word.

10	mark	**11**	start	**12**	hard
	_____		_____		_____
	_____		_____		_____
	_____		_____		_____

Home

Name _____

You love corn a lot.
But I love it more.
We buy popcorn at the movies
And sweet corn at the store.

Food List

▶ Read **each riddle. Answer** it with a word that **rhymes** with the word beside the riddle. **Print it** on the line.

RULE

An **r** after a vowel makes the vowel sound different from the usual short or long sound. You can hear the **or** sound in **corn** and **more**.

1. Something we can pop and eat _____ | horn |

2. Something on a unicorn _____ | born |

3. Something we eat with _____ | cork |

4. Something with rain, wind, and thunder _____ | form |

5. Something we can play or watch _____ | port |

6. Something sharp on a rose _____ | born |

7. Something beside the sea _____ | tore |

8. Something to close up a bottle _____ | pork |

9. Something that gives us light _____ | porch |

Help the horse get to the barn. **Find** the words in the maze with **ar** and **or**. **Follow** them to get to the barn. **Write** each word on the line beside the puzzle.

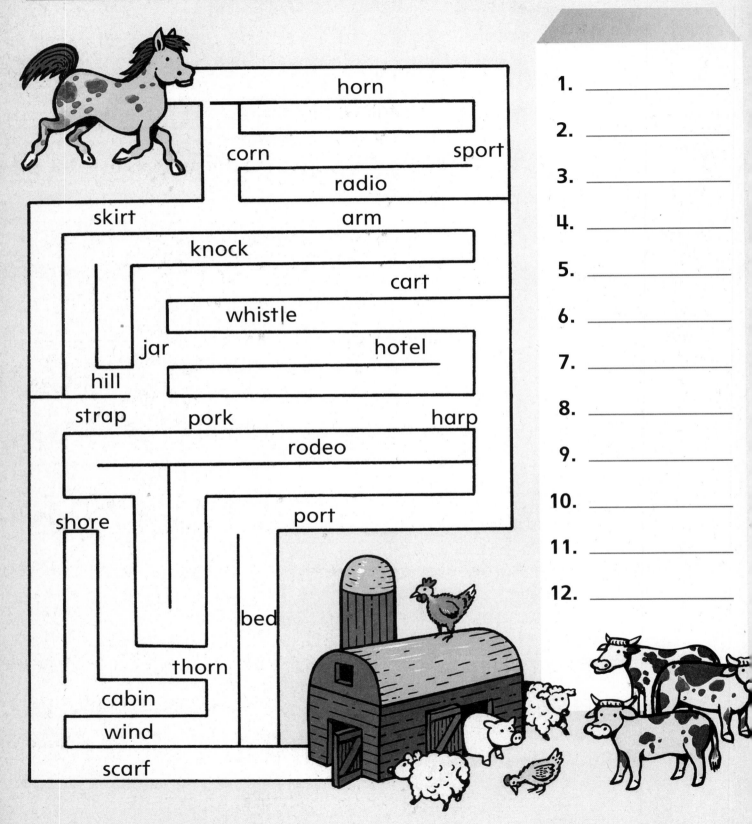

horn

corn   sport

radio

skirt   arm

knock

cart

whistle

jar   hotel

hill

strap   pork   harp

rodeo

shore   port

bed

thorn

cabin

wind

scarf

1. _____

2. _____

3. _____

4. _____

5. _____

6. _____

7. _____

8. _____

9. _____

10. _____

11. _____

12. _____

Review words with ar, or

Home

Have your child put the words in the list in two groups: *ar* words and *or* words.

Name _____

See that bird in the old fir tree?
She'll turn around and chirp at me.
She chirps and chirps her song all day
I hope she never ever goes away.

▶ **Circle** each word that has the same vowel sound as the name of the picture.

1 ir

bird

first
fork
skirt
shirt
girl

2 ur

turtle

curb
purse
card
nurse
fur

3 er

fern

batter
letter
hammer
park
clerk

▶ **Find** the name of each picture in the words above. **Print** the name on the line.

4

_____

5

_____

6

_____

7

_____

8

_____

9

_____

10

_____

11

_____

▶ **Circle the name of the picture. Print an X in the box that has the same vowel with r.**

1
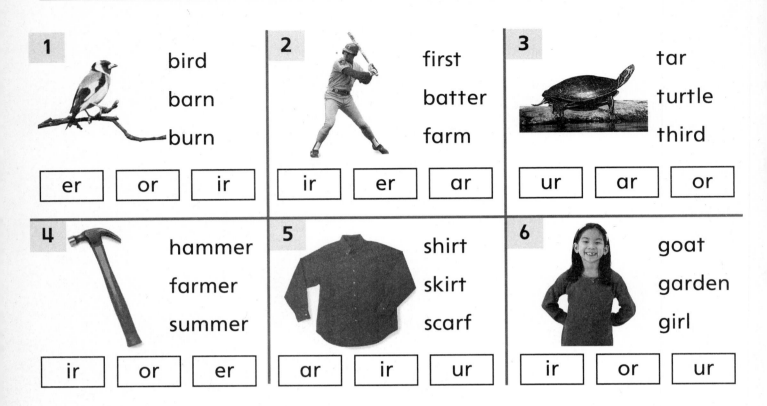
bird
barn
burn

er	or	ir

2
first
batter
farm

ir	er	ar

3
tar
turtle
third

ur	ar	or

4
hammer
farmer
summer

ir	or	er

5
shirt
skirt
scarf

ar	ir	ur

6
goat
garden
girl

ir	or	ur

▶ **Circle the word that will finish the sentence. Print it on the line.**

7. Cats have _____ and purr.　　far　fur

8. Birds have feathers and _____.　　cheat　chirp

9. Turtles _____ up in their shells.　　curl　car

10. Fish have fins and swim in the _____.　　river　hurt

11. Worms wiggle and live in _____.　　burn　dirt

12. Have you _____ wondered why?　　other　ever

Lesson 60
Words with ir, er, ur

Ask your child to say the word that names the picture and identify the vowel sound with r.

Name _____

store	never	turn	dirt
first	evergreen	forty	started

1. This is the _____ tree I ever planted.

2. It is a fir tree called an _____.

3. That means it will _____ change colors.

4. We bought it at a plant _____.

5. We _____ by digging a deep hole.

6. Afterwards we put the _____ back in the hole.

7. It is my _____ to water the tree today.

8. In _____ years, this tree will be huge.

▶ Write each word from the box on the tree that shows its vowel sound.

ar

or

ir

er

ur

1. part _____ ar _____ 1

2. verse _____ _____

3. turn _____ _____

4. pork _____ _____

5. first _____ _____

6. party _____ _____

7. third _____ _____

8. bark _____ _____

9. fern _____ _____

10. storm _____ _____

11. her _____ _____

12. chirp _____ _____

13. park _____ _____

14. horse _____ _____

15. fur _____ _____

16. skirt _____ _____

17. curb _____ _____

18. short _____ _____

19. purse _____ _____

20. under _____ _____

21. hard _____ _____

22. burn _____ _____

1. car   **2.** horn   **3.** bird   **4.** hammer   **5.** turtle

Lesson 61
Review words with ar, or, ir, er, ur

 Home
Say a word on this page and ask your child to name other words that have the same vowel followed by *r*.

Name _____

Phonics & Spelling

Say and **spell** each word below. Then **print** the word in the basket where it belongs.

Word List

shoe	beach	truck	wheel	car	girl
write	thorn	why	chair	wrong	nurse
knock	fork	knob	wish	bath	block

sh

1. _____
2. _____

th

3. _____
4. _____

wh

5. _____
6. _____

ch

7. _____
8. _____

ck

9. _____
10. _____

kn

11. _____
12. _____

ir, ur

13. _____
14. _____

wr

15. _____
16. _____

ar, or

17. _____
18. _____

Phonics & Writing

▶ Pretend that someone you know just won a prize for growing the biggest pumpkin in town. Write a story about it for the newspaper. Use some of the words in the box.

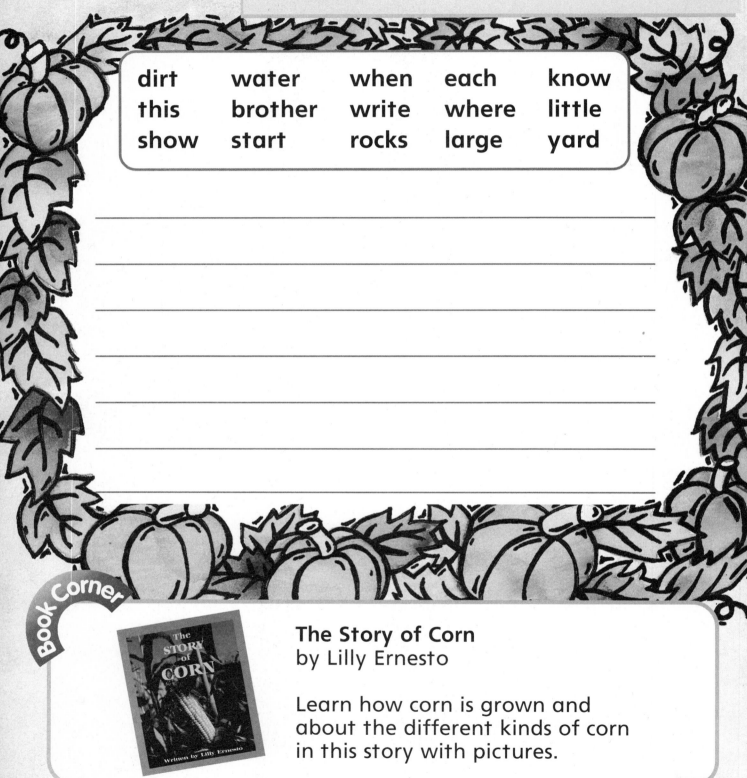

dirt	water	when	each	know
this	brother	write	where	little
show	start	rocks	large	yard

_____

_____

_____

_____

_____

_____

Book Corner

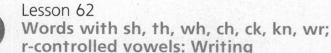

The Story of Corn
by Lilly Ernesto

Learn how corn is grown and about the different kinds of corn in this story with pictures.

Lesson 62
Words with sh, th, wh, ch, ck, kn, wr; r-controlled vowels: Writing

Home Ask your child to spell one word from each basket on page 133.

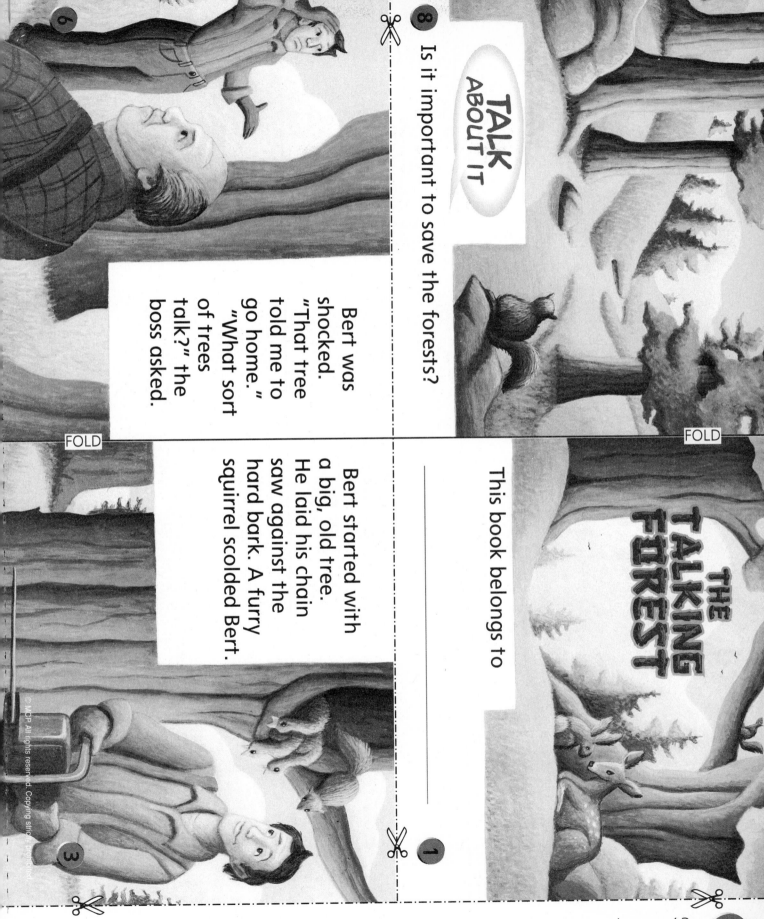

6

8 ✂

Is it important to save the forests?

TALK ABOUT IT

Bert was
shocked.
"That tree
told me to
go home."
"What sort
of trees
talk?" the
boss asked.

FOLD

Bert started with
a big, old tree.
He laid his chain
saw against the
hard bark. A furry
squirrel scolded Bert.

This book belongs to

_____

FOLD

THE TALKING FOREST

3

1 ✂

✂

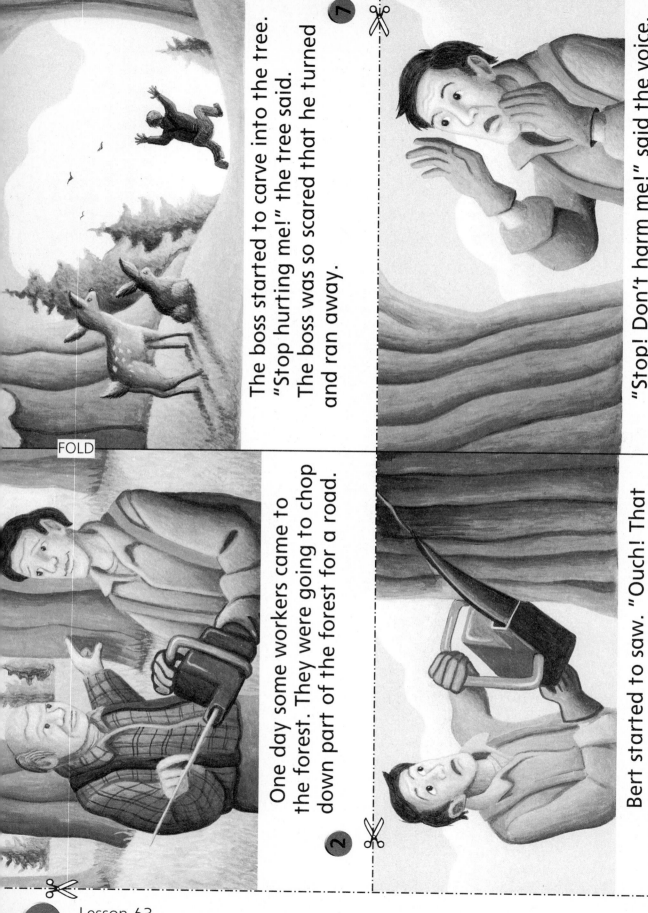

7

The boss started to carve into the tree. "Stop hurting me!" the tree said. The boss was so scared that he turned and ran away.

5

"Stop! Don't harm me!" said the voice. "Who said that?" Bert blurted out. "I did," said the tree. "Go back. Do not chop down the forest."

FOLD

FOLD

2

One day some workers came to the forest. They were going to chop down part of the forest for a road.

4

Bert started to saw. "Ouch! That hurt!" said a voice. Bert turned around. No one was there, so he started to saw again.

Name _____

 Fill in the bubble beside the name of each picture.

1
- ○ nice
- ○ mice
- ○ rice

2
- ○ giraffe
- ○ goat
- ○ giant

3
- ○ turn
- ○ train
- ○ turkey

4
- ○ popcorn
- ○ cupcake
- ○ pencil

5
- ○ beach
- ○ dirt
- ○ bird

6
- ○ clock
- ○ cherry
- ○ check

7
- ○ block
- ○ black
- ○ blot

8
- ○ sneak
- ○ snake
- ○ snore

9
- ○ skunk
- ○ skate
- ○ skill

10
- ○ bun
- ○ bunny
- ○ baby

11
- ○ try
- ○ cry
- ○ shy

12
- ○ ship
- ○ shop
- ○ shell

13
- ○ trunk
- ○ think
- ○ thirteen

14
- ○ chair
- ○ table
- ○ turtle

15
- ○ wrap
- ○ write
- ○ wriggle

Lesson 64

Compounds; le; hard and soft c, g; blends; vowel y; digraphs; r-controlled vowels: Checkup

137

Find the word in the box that will finish each sentence. **Print** it on the line.

knife	snake	garden	Maybe
farm	basket	pepper	who
corn	broccoli	fresh	glad

1. Many kinds of vegetables grow on a _____.

2. First, let's look in the _____.

3. The _____ is green and bushy.

4. We need a _____ to cut the stalks.

5. We can put this green _____ in a salad.

6. _____ I can eat one of the carrots now.

7. Oh! A green _____ just slid under a rock.

8. Let's go pick some sweet yellow _____!

9. We can put it in this straw _____.

10. Vegetables taste best when they are _____.

11. I'm _____ it's almost time to eat.

12. Now _____ will cook them for us?

Lesson 64

138

Compounds; le; hard and soft c, g; blends; vowel y; digraphs; r-controlled vowels: Checkup

Ask your child to make up new sentences containing some of the words from the box.

Home

COUNTDOWN

9
The spaceship is ready.

8
The countdown is steady.

7
The green lights all glow.

6
All systems are go.

5
The crew is all set.

4
So start up the jets.

3
Big engines roar!

2
Only two seconds more.

1
We're set to lift off.

0
!

What do you say when a spaceship takes off?

 **THINK!** **Do you think taking off in a spaceship would be exciting? Why or why not?**

Home Letter

Dear Family,

Your child will be blasting off and exploring space as our class studies contractions, word endings, and suffixes.

At-Home Activities

Here are some activities you and your child might like to do together.

▶ Ask your child to draw a picture of outer space. Then make a list together of the things included. Point out any plurals in the list such as planets, stars, comets, and moons.

▶ With your child look through newspapers and magazines for articles about space. Read the articles and circle words with contractions (we've, can't) and suffixes (darkness, slowly).

Book Corner

You and your child might enjoy reading these books together. Look for them in your local library.

The Moon and You
by E.C. Krupp
This book provides young readers with a light-hearted introduction to the moon.

Moongame
by Frank Asch
In this enchanting story, Bear learns to play hide-and-seek with the moon—and with surprising results!

Sincerely,

Name _____

I'll build a rocket.
We'll go to the moon.
We'll explore outer space.
But, you'll be home by noon.

RULE

A **contraction** is a short way of writing two words. It is formed by putting two words together and leaving out one or more letters. An apostrophe (') is used to show where something is left out. Some contractions are formed with the word **will**.

I will = I'll

▶ **Print a word from the box that means the same as the two words beside each line.**

| you'll | they'll | she'll |
| we'll | I'll | he'll |

1. I will _____

2. he will _____

3. we will _____

4. they will _____

5. she will _____

6. you will _____

▶ **Print the short form of the two underlined words in each sentence.**

7. <u>I will</u> get in the boat after you. _____

8. <u>He will</u> climb aboard next. _____

9. <u>She will</u> join us, too. _____

10. <u>They will</u> hop in for the ride. _____

11. All aboard? Oh, no! <u>We will</u> sink! _____

Print **a word from the box** that means the same as the two words beside each line.

can't	couldn't	weren't	doesn't	don't
didn't	aren't	isn't	won't	haven't

1. are not _____

2. do not _____

3. did not _____

4. will not _____

5. were not _____

6. is not _____

7. could not _____

8. can not _____

9. does not _____

10. have not _____

Print **two words** that mean the same as each underlined word.

11. Mitten the kitten <u>can't</u> get down from the tree.

_____

12. She <u>isn't</u> brave enough to climb down.

_____

13. She <u>doesn't</u> know what to do.

_____

14. We <u>didn't</u> have any problem getting her down.

_____

15. "<u>Aren't</u> you a lucky kitten to have friends to help?"

_____

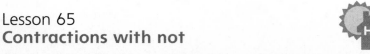

With your child, take turns making up contractions with the words *will* and *not*.

Name _____

Circle **two words in each sentence that can be made into one of the contractions in the box. Print the contraction on the line.**

he is = he's	That is = That's	it is = it's
she is = she's	It is = It's	

1. It is Rocky's birthday. _____

2. What a surprise he is going to get! _____

3. Jess has his gift, but she is hiding it. _____

4. Do you think it is something
Rocky wants? _____

5. What will Rocky get? Look at the
picture at the top. That is what
Rocky wants the most. _____

**Why does Jess hide
Rocky's present?**

Lesson 66
Contractions with is

RULE

Some contractions are formed with the word **have.**

You have = You've
I have = I've
We have = We've
They have = They've

1

I have made you smile.

_____ made you smile.

2

We have shown you tricks.

_____ shown you tricks.

3

They have tossed a ball with their noses.

_____ tossed a ball with their noses.

4

You have had a good time.

_____ had a good time.

 **Where did these things happen?**

Lesson 66
Contractions with have

Write contractions and have your child write the two words that make each one.

Name _____

 Print two words that mean the same as the underlined word in each sentence.

1. <u>Let's</u> have a party. _____

2. <u>We'll</u> ask our friends to come. _____

3. <u>I'm</u> going to pop popcorn. _____

4. <u>He's</u> going to bring some lemonade. _____

5. <u>She's</u> going to bring some cupcakes. _____

6. <u>They're</u> going to bring games. _____

7. <u>We're</u> going to have fun! _____

 Print the contraction that means the same as the two words beside the line.

8. you are _____

9. I am _____

10. let us _____

11. we are _____

12. he is _____

13. I will _____

14. she is _____

15. it is _____

16. they are _____

17. we will _____

18. they will _____

19. he will _____

a. we're	**b.** you'll	**c.** it's	**d.** can't	**e.** I'm
f. he's	**g.** won't	**h.** let's	**i.** don't	**j.** she's
k. you're	**l.** isn't	**m.** he'll	**n.** we'll	**o.** I'll
p. I've	**q.** they'll	**r.** she'll	**s.** we've	**t.** aren't

1. we will _____ **2.** we are _____ **3.** will not _____ **4.** he is _____

5. you will _____ **6.** let us _____ **7.** can not _____ **8.** it is _____

9. is not _____ **10.** you are _____ **11.** they will _____ **12.** I am _____

13. do not _____ **14.** I have _____ **15.** she will _____ **16.** she is _____

17. he will _____ **18.** we have _____ **19.** are not _____ **20.** I will _____

Find a word in the box that will finish each sentence. Print it on the line.

Let's
I'm
It's
I'll
don't
we're

21. _____ go skating in the park.

22. _____ time for us to go.

23. I _____ want to be late.

24. I know _____ ready now, are you?

25. _____ help you find your skates.

26. I think _____ going to have fun.

With your child, take turns making up a sentence for each contraction.

Name _____

 **Phonics & Reading** ▶ **Read the letter. Print a contraction on the line to finish each sentence.**

Dear Mom and Dad,
   I can't believe I've been at Space Camp for four days. I'm having so much fun I don't ever want to leave!

   We're being trained like real astronauts. We're learning about rockets and space travel. Yesterday we made models of rockets and launched them. It's hard work. There's so much to remember.

   Today I'm going in the Moonwalk Trainer. It's a special chair that lets you feel what it's like to walk on the moon. I can't wait.

             Love,
             Cara

1. Cara said, "I _____ believe _____ been at Space Camp for four days."

2. "_____ being trained like real astronauts," she said.

3. "_____ hard work. _____ so much to remember."

 **THINK!** **What would you like to learn at Space Camp?**

Pretend **you want to go to Space Camp.
Fill out the** following **form to apply.
Use some of the words in the box.**

it's	space	you've
shuttle	can't	they're
you're	rockets	isn't
I'm	learn	know
I'll	work	fly

Space Camp Application

Name _____

How did you hear about Space Camp?

_____

_____

What do you think you'll do at Space Camp?

_____

_____

Why do you want to go to Space Camp?

_____

_____

Lesson 68
Review contractions: Writing

Home

Ask your child to tell what words make
the contractions in the list above.

Name _____

Games, books, brushes,
Sandwiches and candy bars.
What other things shall I pack
For a spaceship trip to Mars?

▶ Circle the word that will finish each
sentence. Print it on the line.

RULE

When **s** or **es** is added to a word it forms the plural. Plural means "more than one." If a word ends in **x, z, ss, sh,** or **ch,** usually add **es** to make it mean more than one. For other words just add **s.**

one brush   two **brushes**
one sandwich   many **sandwiches**
one book   three **books**

---

1   At the zoo we saw some

    seal   seals

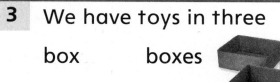

_____.

2   We like to eat fresh

    peach   peaches

_____.

---

3   We have toys in three

    box   boxes

_____.

4   June will use a

    brush   brushes

_____.

---

5   Ed's mom gave him a

    cap   caps

_____.

6   Just look at those

    dog   dogs

_____.

---

7   Look at those shiny

    star   stars

_____.

8   The box was used for

    mitten   mittens

_____.

Lesson 69
Plural endings -s, -es

149

Read each shopping list. Finish each word by adding the ending s or es. Print the ending on the line.

1

Steve's List

1. 2 book _____ to read

2. 3 paintbrush _____

3. 6 red pencil _____

4. 2 jar _____ of paste

2

Peggy's List

1. 5 block _____

2. 2 box _____ of clay

3. 3 top _____ to spin

4. 2 puzzle _____

3

Pam's List

1. 8 dish _____

2. 8 cup _____

3. 4 glass _____

4. 2 patch _____ for jeans

4

Ron's List

1. 7 apple _____

2. 5 peach _____

3. 4 sandwich _____

4. 2 bunch _____ of grapes

Home Ask your child to make up a list of objects using endings -s, -es.

Name _____

Floating and bobbing,
We drifted in space.
We tried hard to run,
But just stayed in one place.

A **base word** is a word to which the ending **ing** or **ed** can be added to form a new word.

float + ing = floating
drift + ed = drifted

▶ Add **ing** to each base word. Print the new word on the line.

1. sleep _____   2. jump _____

3. play _____   4. help _____

5. start _____   6. work _____

7. fish _____   8. turn _____

▶ Add **ing** to the word beside each sentence. Print the new word on the line.

9. We are _____ for the bus.

10. Doris and Mark are _____ rope.

11. Sam is _____ for the bus.

12. Bart's dog is _____ with him.

13. Terry is _____ his lunch.

14. Meg is _____ a book.

15. Now the bus is _____ our corner!

| wait |
| jump |
| look |
| stay |
| hold |
| read |
| turn |

Add **ed** to each base word. **Print** the new word on the line.
Use the new words to finish the sentences.

1 look

_____

2 want

_____

3 help

_____

4 leap

_____

5 fix

_____

6 paint

_____

7. Jess _____ me catch a frog.

8. We _____ a frog for a pet.

9. We _____ everywhere for frogs.

10. Suddenly a frog _____ over a rock.

11. We _____ up a box for a frog home.

Print each base word on the line.

12 locked

_____

13 marched

_____

14 dreamed

_____

15 played

_____

16 cleaned

_____

17 passed

_____

18 watched

_____

19 wanted

_____

20 missed

_____

Lesson 70
Inflectional ending -ed

With your child, take turns acting
out each base word; then add *ed*.

Name _____

► Add **es** or **ed** to the base word in the cap to finish each sentence. **Print** the new word on the line.

1. The girls _____ baseball after school.

2. Randy always watches and _____ for Jean's team to win.

3. The ball comes fast and _____ past Jean's bat. Strike one!

4. The pitcher throws and the ball _____ toward the plate.

5. Jean swings as the ball _____ by.

6. This time Jean has not _____.

7. Randy _____ up out of his seat.

8. He _____ until he was hoarse.

play

wish

brush

buzz

pass

miss

jump

cheer

► Add **s** or **es** to each base word in the box. **Print** the new word on the line.

| see | fox | bush | patch | mail | line |

9. _____   10. _____   11. _____

12. _____   13. _____   14. _____

Circle the word that will finish each sentence. **Print it** on the line.

1. Dad goes _____ in the stream.

   fishing
   fished

2. While the time _____, he looks around.

   passes
   passing

3. Yesterday some quacking ducks _____ by.

   floats
   floated

4. Three baby ducks _____ their mother.

   followed
   following

5. Frogs were _____ in and out of the water.

   jumping
   jumps

6. They were _____ for bugs to eat.

   looking
   looked

7. Some birds were _____ each other.

   helped
   helping

8. While one _____ the nest, the other looked for food.

   watched
   watching

9. They _____ to feed their hungry babies.

   needs
   needed

10. Dad _____ looking around as much as he likes fishing.

    liking
    likes

THINK! What did Dad see while he was fishing?

Home   Take turns identifying the base word and the ending for each circled word.

Name _____

> **Add ing** to the base word in the box.
> **Print the new word** on the line.

RULE

When a short vowel word ends in a single consonant, usually double the consonant before adding **ing**.
stop + ing = stopping

1. Maria and Jess were _____ to go shopping.

2. First they went _____ in the park.

3. Children were _____ on the swings.

4. Some horseback riders were

   _____ around.

5. Other people were _____ along a path.

6. They saw two bunnies _____ by.

7. A turtle was _____ at a bug.

8. A man was _____ hot dogs.

9. His dog was _____ for one.

10. "_____ in the park was fun," said Maria.

11. "Now let's go _____," Jess said.

plan

jog

swing

trot

walk

hop

snap

roast

beg

Run

shop

 **What time of year is this?**

Lesson 72
Inflectional ending -ing

155

Add ed to the word beside each sentence to make it tell about the past. **Print** the word on the line.

1. My dog _____ his tail when I got home.

2. He _____ up on me with a happy smile.

3. When I _____ him, my hand got muddy.

4. "Wags, you need to be _____!"

5. I _____ him up.

6. Then I _____ him in the tub.

7. He _____ around in the water.

8. He _____ water everywhere!

9. I laughed as I _____ him.

10. When Wags _____, he was clean but I was a mess!

11. I _____ up the mess.

12. Then I _____ with Wags.

wag

hop

pat

scrub

pick

dip

jump

splash

watch

stop

clean

play

 **THINK!** **How do you think Wags got muddy?**

 Home Take turns with your child saying a word and spelling it with the -ed ending.

Name _____

> **Circle** the word that finishes each sentence. **Print** it on the line.

RULE

If a word ends with a silent **e**, drop the **e** before adding **ing** or **ed**.
I **bake** cookies with my mom.
We **baked** cookies yesterday.
We are **baking** cookies today, too.

1. Yesterday I _____ to the park.

2. Then I _____ home.

3. Today I am _____ with friends.

4. We are _____ for lunch.

jogged
jogging

walked
walking

skating
skated

stopped
stopping

> **Read** each pair of sentences. **Add ing** or **ed** to the base word. **Print** the new word on the line.

clean

5. Today Dad is _____ the garage.

   He _____ the car yesterday.

save

6. I am _____ my money to buy a bike.

   Last week I _____ almost $3.00.

wag

7. Last night my dog was happy, so she _____

   her tail. She is _____ her tail now, too.

Add ing to each base word. Print the new word on the line.

1. ride _____

2. fry _____

3. rub _____

4. hide _____

5. frame _____

6. dig _____

7. take _____

8. jump _____

9. poke _____

10. ship _____

11. pack _____

12. quit _____

Add ed to each base word. Print the new word on the line.

13. pin _____

14. rock _____

15. chase _____

16. hop _____

17. march _____

18. bake _____

19. wish _____

20. drop _____

21. hope _____

22. quack _____

Lesson 73
Inflectional endings -ing, -ed

Home

With your child take turns choosing a word, adding an ending, and using it in a sentence.

Name _____

> Read **the story.** Print **a word that ends in s, es, ed, or ing on the line to finish each sentence.**

Seeing Stars

Have you ever looked up in the sky and wondered about the stars? Some stars are huge masses of fire like the sun. Many of these stars may have worlds traveling around them just as the Earth we live on travels around our sun. Astronomers have discovered planets around some stars.

We are not traveling alone. Some of the stars you see are not stars at all. They are other planets going around our sun. Nine planets have been discovered so far. Other planets may be waiting far out in space for someone to find them.

1. Have you ever wondered about the _____ ?

2. Some stars are huge _____ of fire.

3. Nine planets have been _____ around our sun.

4. Other planets may be _____ to be found.

Do you think other planets will be discovered? Why or why not?

Lesson 74

Review -s, -es, -ed, -ing: Reading

159

Imagine you are an astronaut on a spacecraft traveling to other planets. Part of your job is to write in your log book what happens every day. Write about what you saw today. Use some of the words in the box.

wanted	likes	wishes	passes	watched
stars	colors	planets	seeing	traveled
rings	moons	waiting	space	floating

Date _____

_____

_____

_____

_____

_____

_____

_____

_____

_____

_____

Home

Ask your child to find words with -s, -es, -ed, -ing in the story on page 159.

Name _____

Moon rocks are colorful,
Moon dust is wonderful.
But I must be truthful,
They aren't very useful!

▶ Add **the ending** **ful** **to each base word.**
Print **the new word on the line. Use the**
new words to finish the sentences.

1. care _____

2. cheer _____

3. wonder _____

4. use _____

5. Pablo thought a skateboard would be very _____.

6. He promised to be _____ if he got one.

7. His family looked _____ when they gave
him his gift.

8. It was a skateboard! What a _____ gift!

▶ Draw **a box around each base word.**

9. u s e f u l

10. h o p e f u l

11. r e s t f u l

12. h a r m f u l

13. f e a r f u l

14. h e l p f u l

15. p l a y f u l

16. c a r e f u l

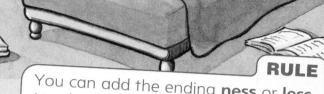

What's that in the darkness?
A space monster in flight?
I'm almost fearless,
But I'll turn on the light!

Add **less** or **ness** to each base word. Print **the new word on the line. Use the new words to finish the sentences.**

RULE

You can add the ending **ness** or **less** to a base word to make a new word.

dark + ness = darkness
fear + less = fearless

less

1. use _____

2. sleep _____

3. harm _____

4. fear _____

ness

5. thick _____

6. dark _____

7. loud _____

8. sharp _____

9. It is _____ to tell me the bear is harmless.

10. I am not brave and _____.

11. When I think about the bear, I'm _____.

12. The bear's eyes are glowing in the _____.

13. The _____ of its snarls worries me.

14. I can almost feel the _____ of its teeth.

15. I see the _____ of its strong legs.

Write base words and suffixes on separate cards and have your child match them.

Name _____

Slowly the sun rises.
Quickly the sky gets bright.
Slowly the sun will set again,
When it's nearly night.

▶ Add **the ending ly to each base word.**
Print the new word on the line.

> **RULE**
> Add the ending **ly** to a base word
> to make a new word.
> **slow + ly = slowly**

1. glad _____   2. swift _____

3. soft _____   4. brave _____

5. loud _____   6. slow _____

7. love _____   8. near _____

▶ Circle **each ly ending in the sentences. Print the base**
words on the lines.

9. Tigers walk softly.   _____

10. Lions roar bravely.   _____

11. Monkeys screech loudly.   _____

12. Turtles crawl slowly.   _____

13. Deer run swiftly.   _____

14. I watch them at the
    zoo gladly.   _____

15. The zoo near my house
    is lovely.   _____

Match the base word in the first column with the new word in the second column. Print the letter on the line.

1

_____ quick   **a.** slowly

_____ sweet   **b.** quickly

_____ slow   **c.** sweetly

_____ loud   **d.** loudly

_____ nice   **e.** nicely

2

_____ glad   **a.** softly

_____ soft   **b.** nearly

_____ near   **c.** lovely

_____ love   **d.** gladly

_____ brave   **e.** bravely

3

_____ use   **a.** playful

_____ play   **b.** handful

_____ cheer   **c.** useful

_____ hand   **d.** harmful

_____ harm   **e.** cheerful

4

_____ care   **a.** fearless

_____ sleeve   **b.** helpless

_____ fear   **c.** jobless

_____ job   **d.** careless

_____ help   **e.** sleeveless

5

_____ home   **a.** sleepless

_____ sleep   **b.** cheerless

_____ use   **c.** homeless

_____ wire   **d.** useless

_____ cheer   **e.** wireless

6

_____ good   **a.** softness

_____ dark   **b.** sadness

_____ kind   **c.** darkness

_____ sad   **d.** goodness

_____ soft   **e.** kindness

Lesson 76
Review suffixes -ly, -ful, -less, -ness

Home

With your child, think of other words to add to the boxes.

Name _____

Add an ending from the box to finish the word in each sentence. Print it on the line. Trace the whole word.

ly
ful
less
ness

1. Polly was usually brave and _fear_____ .

2. Today she was _lone_____ in her new school.

3. She thought of her old friends with _sad_____ .

4. She remembered all their _kind_____ .

5. _Sudden_____ she saw some girls smiling at her.

6. Now she felt more _cheer_____ .

Read the words in the box. Print each word next to its definition.

7. with no fear _____

8. full of play _____

9. in a safe way _____

10. being dark _____

fearless
darkness
safely
playful

Say **and** spell **the words in the tic-tac-toe grids.** Follow **the directions for each grid.** Draw **straight lines through three words across, up and down, or on a diagonal to win.**

1 Match **ly** words.

blasting	sunless	lovely
stars	biggest	slowly
hopeful	roared	nicely

2 Match **ness** words.

darkness	cheerful	sweetly
longest	softness	rockets
fearful	stronger	coldness

3 Match **ful** words.

warmly	swiftness	joyful
smarter	joined	trying
careful	helpful	wishful

4 Match **less** words.

kindness	careless	playful
nearly	moonless	starting
lighter	fearless	quickly

Lesson 77
Review Suffixes -ly, -ful, -less, -ness

Home

Ask your child to read aloud the words that won each tic-tac-toe game.

Name _____

That star on the left is very bright,
But the brighter star is on the right.
Which are the brightest stars of all,
The ones in the sky or the ones that fall?

RULE

You can add the ending **er** to a base word to make a new word that tells about two things. Add the ending **est** to tell about more than two things.

bright   brighter   brightest

▶ Add **the ending er and est to each word. Print the new words on the lines.**

er   **est**

1. near _____   _____

2. long _____   _____

3. fast _____   _____

4. dark _____   _____

5. thick _____   _____

6. deep _____   _____

7. soft _____   _____

▶ Draw **a picture to show the meaning of each word.**

8	**9**	**10**
long	longer	longest

Finish each sentence by adding er or est to each base word. Use er to tell about two things. Use est to tell about more than two things. Print the new word on the line.

1. tall  Meg is ＿＿＿＿＿＿ than Jay.

2. hard  The rock is ＿＿＿＿＿＿ than the soap.

3. fast  The horse is the ＿＿＿＿＿＿ of the three.

4. long  The top fish is the ＿＿＿＿＿＿.

5. cold 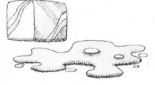 Ice is ＿＿＿＿＿＿ than water.

6. small  The ant is the ＿＿＿＿＿＿.

Lesson 78
Suffixes -er, -est

 Home

With your child, take turns using -er and -est words to compare things at home.

Name _____

Add **er** and **est** to each word.
Print **the new words on the lines.**

er   est

1. silly   _____   _____

2. happy   _____   _____

3. windy   _____   _____

4. fluffy   _____   _____

Finish **each sentence by adding er or est to the base word in the box.**

5. Today was Justin's _____ kind of day.

6. He got to the bus stop _____ than he did yesterday.

7. It was _____ than it had been all week.

8. He made up the _____ joke he could.

9. The other kids said it was the

   _____ one they had heard.

| happy |

| early |

| sunny |

| silly |

| funny |

RULE

When a word ends in **y** after a consonant, change the **y** to **i** before adding **es**.

story + es = stories

Circle the name of each picture.

1

daisy   daisies

2

cherry   cherries

3

lily   lilies

**Use the rule to add es to the word beside each sentence.
Finish the sentence by printing the new word on the line.**

4. We wrote _____ for our class book.

5. Mine was about my dog's new _____.

6. Lily wrote about planting _____.

7. Penny's story was about raising _____.

8. Carol told us about picking _____.

9. Marty gave ideas for birthday _____.

10. Jerry told how to take care of _____.

11. Tony wrote about his collection of _____.

12. When we finished, we made extra _____.

story

puppy

daisy

bunny

cherry

party

pony

penny

copy

Home

Take turns picking a base word and using it in a sentence with ending *-es*.

Name _____

Add endings to make the words mean more than one.

1	bunny	**2**	city	**3**	box
_____		_____		_____	
4	lily	**5**	dress	**6**	pony
_____		_____		_____	

Circle the word that will finish each sentence. Print it on the line. Then print the name of each picture below.

7. Mary's birthday _____ was fun.   party   parties

8. Her dad read scary _____.   story   stories

9. We tossed _____ into bottles.   penny   pennies

10. Instead of cake, we ate _____ pie.   cherry   cherries

11. We got little _____ to take home.   candy   candies

12 	**13** 	**14** 
_____	_____	_____

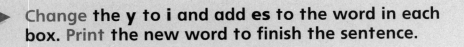

Change the y to i and add es to the word in each box. Print the new word to finish the sentence.

1. Farms are different from _____.

2. Sometimes my friends and our _____ visit a farm.

3. Sometimes there are lots of _____ in the fields.

4. Some _____ grow by the streams.

5. We like to ride the _____.

6. There are many different animal _____.

7. It's fun to play with the _____.

8. We usually see some _____.

9. Fruits and _____ grow on farms.

10. We climb trees to pick _____.

11. I like to write _____ about our trips to the country.

12. I give _____ to my friends to read.

| city |
| family |
| daisy |
| lily |
| pony |
| baby |
| bunny |
| puppy |
| berry |
| cherry |
| story |
| copy |

THINK! Where does the family in the story live?

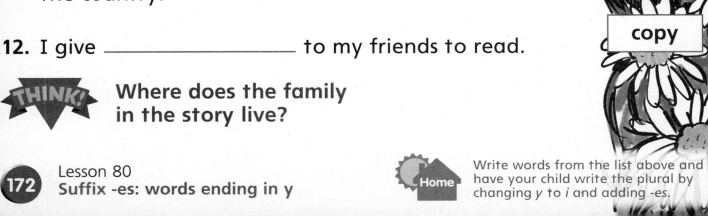

Home Write words from the list above and have your child write the plural by changing y to i and adding -es.

Name _____

Phonics & Spelling

▶ Print the word next to the comet with the same ending.
Print two contractions next to the last comet.

Word List

coldness	going	can't	thoughtful	lovely	funnier
blasted	waiting	darkness	deepest	glasses	bushes
happiest	wanted	slowly	careful	brighter	they're

1. ed _____   _____

2. ing _____   _____

3. ly _____   _____

4. ful _____   _____

5. es _____   _____

6. ness _____   _____

7. er _____   _____

8. est _____   _____

9. contractions _____   _____

Contractions, endings, suffixes: Spelling

search for dinosaur bones?   Introduction

Home Letter

Dear Family,

In the next few weeks we'll be learning about vowel pairs, digraphs, and diphthongs while we explore the wonderful world of dinosaurs.

At-Home Activities

Here are some activities you and your child can do together.

▶ Make a clay model of a dinosaur. Ask your child to identify the parts of the animal and write them down together. Circle words with vowel pairs, digraphs, and diphthongs, such as tail, head, toes, teeth, and mouth.

▶ Look in the library for books about dinosaurs. As you read, point out words that have different vowel sounds, such as round, brown, pool, and coat.

Book Corner

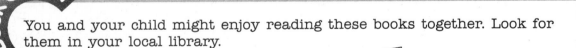

You and your child might enjoy reading these books together. Look for them in your local library.

Holding Onto Sunday
by Kathryn O. Galbraith

One Sunday, Jemma and her father go dinosaur hunting at the museum.

Discovering Dinosaur Babies
by Miriam Schleir

How dinosaurs lived and raised their families, based on recent discoveries of dinosaur eggs, is explained in this fascinating book.

Sincerely,

Name _____

Gail said, "What a rainy day!
Another rainy Saturday!
Let's stay right here and play.
Let's make dinosaurs from clay."

Find the word in the box that names
each picture. **Print** it on the line.

sail	pay	rain	tail	hay
tray	spray	chain	nail	

1 _____

2 _____

3 _____

4 _____

5 _____

6 _____

7 _____

8 _____

9 _____

Find **the word in the box that answers each riddle.**
Print **the word on the line.**

chain	stain	mailbox	hay	pail	rain	tray
hair	paint	chair	train	gray	sail	day

1. I ride on railroad tracks. _____

2. You put letters in me. _____

3. I am a blend of black and white. _____

4. If I start, you put on a raincoat. _____

5. You can sit on me. _____

6. I am made of many links. _____

7. I am part of a boat. _____

8. I am an ink spot on a shirt. _____

9. I am piled in a stack. _____

10. You can use a comb on me. _____

11. You can carry water in me. _____

12. I am spread on a wall. _____

13. You carry food on me. _____

14. I come before night. _____

Lesson 84
Vowel pairs ai, ay: Words in context

Home

With your child, take turns using
each word in the box in a sentence.

Name _____

RULE

Vowel pairs **ee** and **ea** can make the long **e** sound. You can hear the long **e** sound in **jeep** and **seal.**

1

sell
seal
seed

2

bean
bed
bee

3

jeep
jeans
peep

4

leaf
lean
leak

5

jeeps
jeans
jets

6

feed
feet
feel

7

deep
deeds
deer

8

meat
met
team

9

eat
each
ear

10

peach
peace
pear

11

seal
seed
send

12

team
test
teeth

keep	eager	easy	meal
feet	steer	beaver	each
teeth	leaves	seem	seen

1. Have you ever _____ a beaver? _____

2. A _____ likes to chew down trees. _____

3. It makes a _____ of the bark. _____

4. It uses _____ branch to build a dam. _____

5. It only _____ the stump behind. _____

6. A beaver's _____ have to be strong. _____

7. Its webbed _____ help it swim along. _____

8. It uses its tail to _____. _____

9. It's not _____ being a beaver. _____

10. Beavers always _____ to be working. _____

11. They _____ working until all their work is done. _____

12. That's why busy people are often called

    " _____ beavers." _____

 **Why is the beaver so busy?**

 Help your child sort the words according to vowel pairs (*ea* or *ee*).

Name _____

Circle **the word that will finish each sentence.** Print **it on the line.**

1. My friend, _____, and I went to the store.

jay
Joe
jot

2. Along the way, we saw a _____ by the road.

die
doe
day

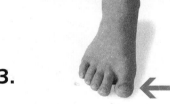

3. When we got there, Joe stubbed his _____.

tie
toe
lie

4. My dog _____ stayed outside.

Moe
my
mine

5. I wanted to buy a new red _____.

tie
toe
lie

6. We all had some _____ when we got home.

pie
pine
pile

THINK! **Why did Moe stay outside?**

Lesson 86
Vowel pairs ie, oe: Words in context

185

Print the name for each picture on the line below it.

boat	rainbow	goat	bow	soap	bowl

1

2

3

4

5

6

Circle the word that will finish each sentence. **Print it** on the line.

7. Isn't it fun to ride in a _____?   boot   boat

8. Sailboats move when the wind _____.   blows   blues

9. You use oars to _____ some boats.   raw   row

10. Tugboats _____ other boats along.   tow   too

11. Steamboats use steam to _____ along the river.   float   floor

 Home Have your child circle the vowel pairs *oa* and *ow* in the words on this page.

Name _____

Phonics & Reading

▶ **Read** the story. **Print** a word with a vowel pair on the line to finish each sentence.

Kay's Surprise

One day Kay's Aunt Jean sent her a surprise—a pet iguana. Kay had never seen anything like it.

It looked like a baby dinosaur. It had a brown and green coat and a long tail. It also had big feet with a sharp little claw on each toe.

Kay got a book about iguanas to read. She learned that iguanas don't eat meat. They need a meal of lettuce once a day. They also like sweet potatoes, apples and oranges. Iguanas need to stay warm and like to lie in the sun. They can also grow to be six feet long!

1. It had a brown and green _____ and a long _____

2. Iguanas need a _____ of lettuce once a _____.

3. They also like _____ potatoes.

THINK! Would an iguana make a good pet? Why or why not?

Phonics & Writing

Pretend you are Kay. Write a note to Aunt Jean to thank her for the surprise. Use some of the words in the box.

neat
toe
sweet
mean
bow
teeth
tail
know
seen
wait

Dear _____

_____

_____

_____

_____

_____

_____

_____

_____

 Home

Have your child circle the vowel pairs in the words in *Kay's Surprise*.

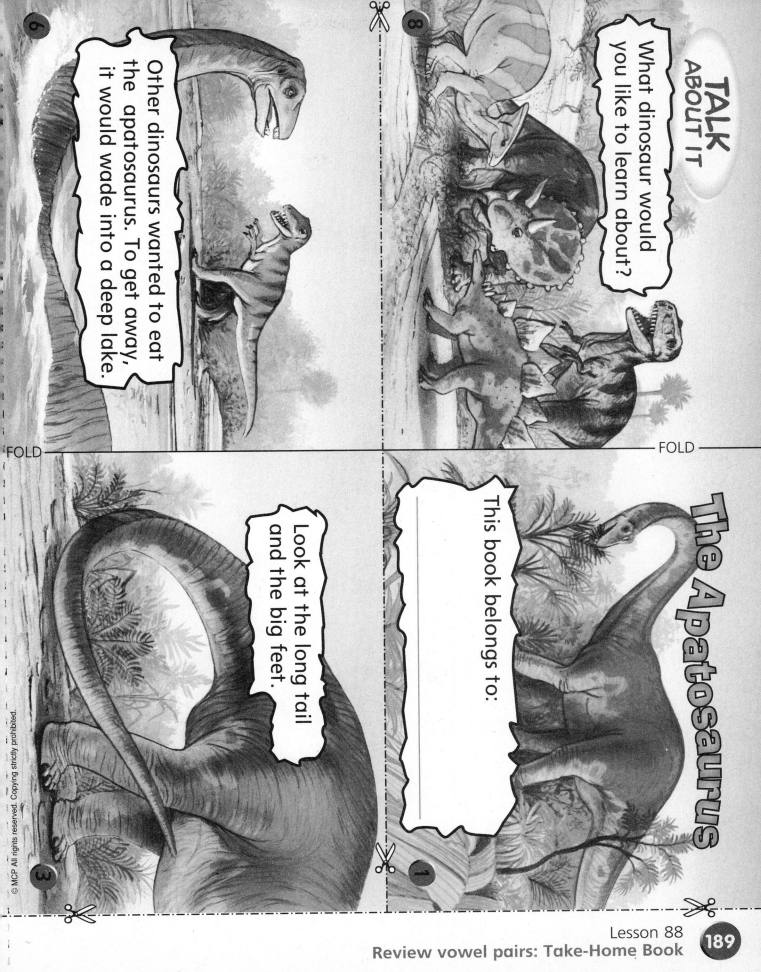

6

Other dinosaurs wanted to eat the apatosaurus. To get away, it would wade into a deep lake.

8

TALK
ABOUT IT

What dinosaur would you like to learn about?

FOLD

FOLD

3

Look at the long tail and the big feet.

1

This book belongs to:

_____

The Apatosaurus

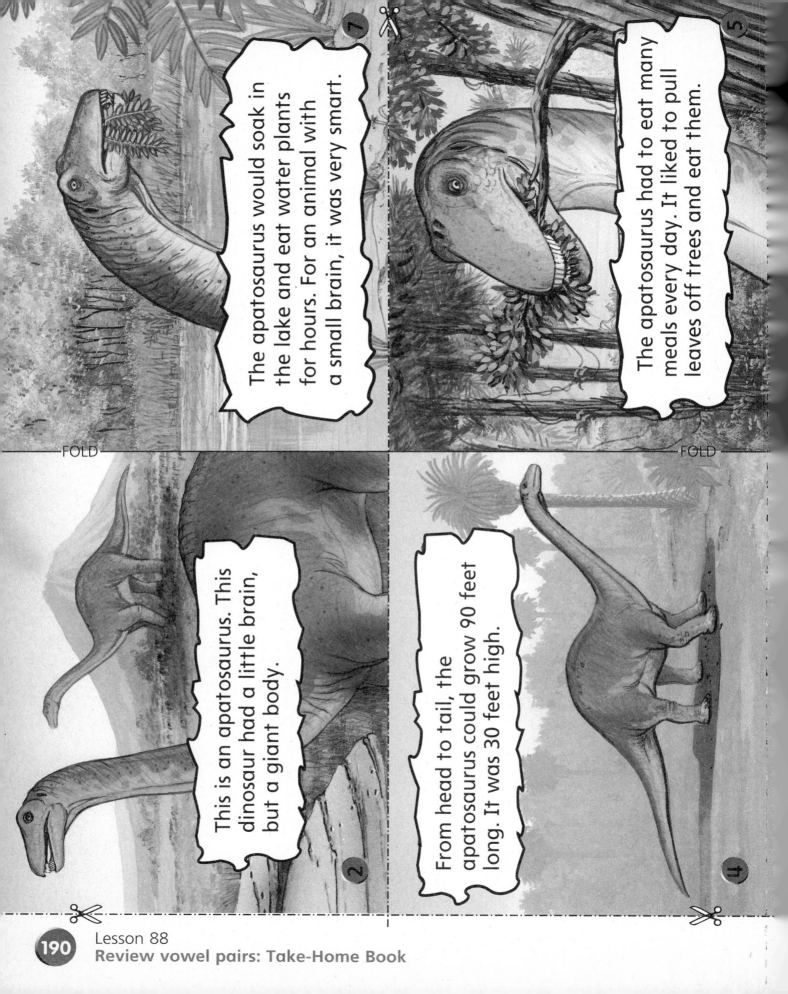

7

The apatosaurus would soak in the lake and eat water plants for hours. For an animal with a small brain, it was very smart.

FOLD

5

The apatosaurus had to eat many meals every day. It liked to pull leaves off trees and eat them.

FOLD

This is an apatosaurus. This dinosaur had a little brain, but a giant body.

2

From head to tail, the apatosaurus could grow 90 feet long. It was 30 feet high.

4

190

Lesson 88
Review vowel pairs: Take-Home Book

Name _____

A tooth here, a foot bone, too.
We use tools to dig and brush.
When you look for dinosaur bones,
You can't be in a rush.

> Circle **the word that will finish each sentence.** Print **it on the line.**

RULE

In a **vowel digraph,** two vowels together can make a long or a short sound, or have a special sound all their own. You can hear the different sounds of the vowel digraph **oo** in **tooth** and **foot.**

1. I felt something _____ in my mouth.

broom
loose

2. Was it a _____?

tool
tooth

3. I ran to my _____.

room
zoo

4. I stood on a _____ to look in the mirror.

spoon
stool

5. My tooth should fall out _____.

moon
soon

6. At _____ it was time for lunch.

soon
noon

7. I took a bite of _____ with my spoon.

food
fool

8. Out came my loose tooth on the _____.

soothe
spoon

9. My friend lost a tooth, _____.

too
zoo

Why do you lose your teeth?

Lesson 89
Vowel digraph oo: Words in context

191

cookie	look	good	stood
book	cook	took	hook

1. I was looking for a good _____.

2. I took a _____ at a cookbook.

3. I _____ in line to pay for the book.

4. Then I _____ my new book home.

5. I decided to _____ something.

6. I took my apron off a _____.

7. I tried a _____ recipe.

8. The cookies were very _____.

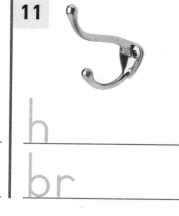

▶ **Print the missing letters of each picture's name. Print the missing letters for a word that rhymes with it. Trace the whole word.**

9	10	11	12
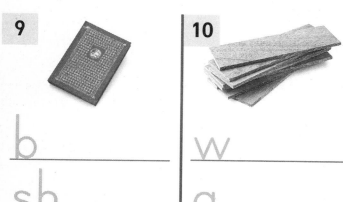		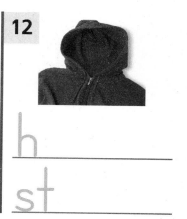	
b_____	w_____	h_____	h_____
sh_____	g_____	br_____	st_____

 Home · With your child, make up a rhyme for each pair of words above.

Name _____

▶ **Find the word in the box that will finish each sentence. Print it on the line.**

ahead	already	breakfast	spread
bread	breath	head	

1. When you wake up, take a deep _____.

2. It will help clear your _____.

3. Now you are ready for _____.

4. Here is some _____ to make toast.

5. You can _____ butter and jam on it.

6. The eggs are _____ made.

7. Go _____ and eat.

▶ **Circle the correct word to finish each sentence.**

8. What is the (feather, weather, leather) like today?

9. Will you need to wear a (sweater, weather, meadow)?

10. Maybe you will need a (ready, heavy, cleanser) coat.

11. Is it cold enough for (bread, thread, leather) boots?

12. Cover your (head, heavy, breakfast) with a warm hat.

13. Now you are (meadow, heavy, ready) to go outside.

1
seat
bread
meat
bean

2
bread
beach
heavy
treat

3
reach
steam
break
great

4
dream
mean
beak
health

5
head
heavy
lean
steak

6
steak
tea
teacher
great

7
beaver
team
leather
beans

8
bread
weather
seal
leather

9
ready
heavy
bread
bean

10
beach
teach
health
reach

11
break
leather
thread
weather

12
meat
great
heat
leak

Home With your child, take turns naming a word that rhymes with each picture name.

Name _____

Find the word in the box that will finish each sentence. Print it on the line.

RULE

The vowel digraphs **au** and **aw** usually have the same sound. You can hear the sound of **au** and **aw** in **August** and **paw**.

| drawing | autumn | straws | haul | August |
| lawn | pause | yawn | crawls | Paula |

1. _____ is a lazy month.

2. We _____ in our work to relax.

3. _____ and I play games in the shade.

4. I water the _____ in the evenings.

5. We _____ the picnic basket to the lake.

6. After swimming, we _____ and nap in the sun.

7. We sip lemonade through _____.

8. My baby brother _____ on the grass.

9. Summer's end is _____ near.

10. Soon _____ will come, and school will start.

 **Why does this family like August?**

Lesson 91
Vowel digraphs au, aw: Words in context

195

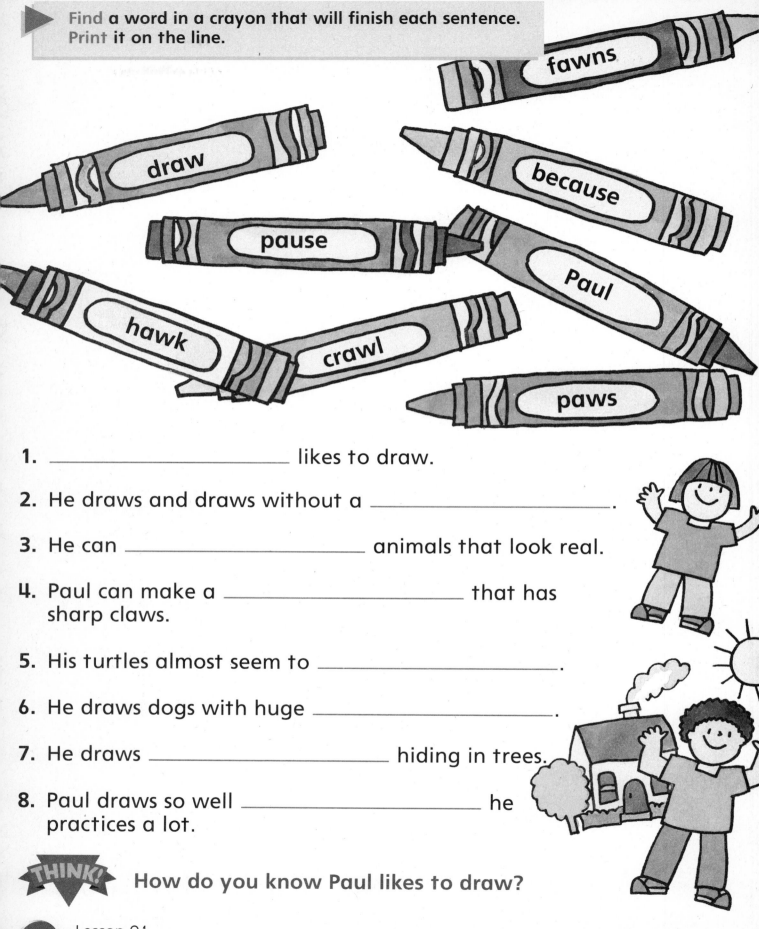

fawns

draw

because

pause

Paul

hawk

crawl

paws

1. _____ likes to draw.

2. He draws and draws without a _____.

3. He can _____ animals that look real.

4. Paul can make a _____ that has sharp claws.

5. His turtles almost seem to _____.

6. He draws dogs with huge _____.

7. He draws _____ hiding in trees.

8. Paul draws so well _____ he practices a lot.

THINK! How do you know Paul likes to draw?

Name _____

Read the words in the bubbles. Print each word under the picture that has the same vowel sound.

cook

broom   hook   head

yawn   claw   pool

break

bread   leaf   team

1

_____

_____

2

_____

_____

3

_____

_____

4

_____

_____

5

_____

_____

6

_____

_____

Say the name of each picture. **Circle** the letters that stand for the vowel sound in the picture's name. Then **print** the letters to finish its name. **Trace** the whole word.

1
aw
oo
ea

s _ _

2
aw
ea
oo

br _ d

3
aw
oo
ea

f _ ther

4
ea
au
oo

sp _ n

5
oo
ea
aw

st _ k

6
au
ea
oo

p _ l

7
oo
au
ea

w _ d

8
aw
oo
ea

str _

9
ea
aw
oo

f _ n

10
aw
ea
oo

j _ ns

11
ea
oo
au

l _ ndry

12
oo
ea
aw

wh _ t

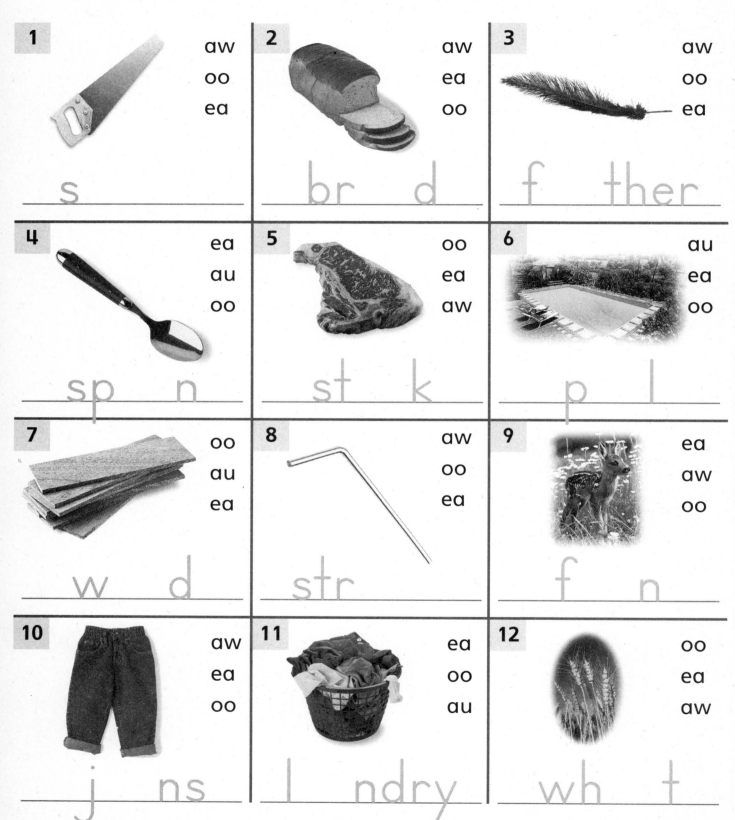

Lesson 92
Review vowel digraphs oo, ea, au, aw

Home

Have your child circle the digraphs in the words on page 197.

Name _____

 **Phonics & Reading**

 Read the newspaper article. **Print** a word with **oo, ea, au,** or **aw** from the story on the line to finish each sentence.

What Really Happened?

Long ago, the heavy feet of giant dinosaurs shook the earth. Then something awful happened. All of these awesome animals died. Scientists are looking for clues to find out what really happened.

Some scientists think a meteor or comet hit the earth, causing great fires. Dust and ash blocked the sun's light and changed the weather. Warm places became cool. Cool places became colder. Plants and small animals died because of the cold. The dinosaurs could not find food.

1. Their _____ feet _____ the earth.

2. A comet may have hit the earth, _____ great fires.

3. These _____ animals died.

 **Why do you think the dinosaurs died?**

Phonics & Writing

Pretend **that you have discovered some dinosaur bones.** Write **a story for your school newspaper to tell people about your discovery.** Use **some of the words in the box.**

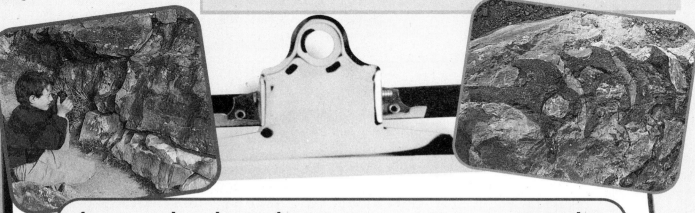

claw	book	heavy	paws	taught
head	draw	because	look	jaw

_____

_____

_____

_____

_____

_____

_____

_____

Home Ask your child to use each of the words in the box in a sentence.

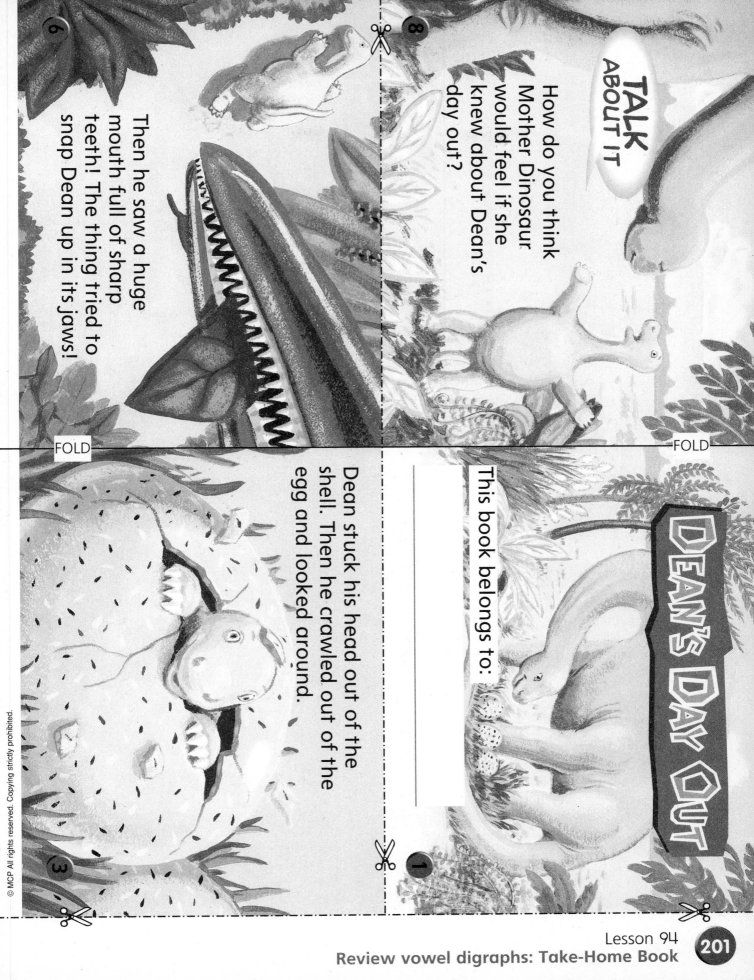

6

Then he saw a huge mouth full of sharp teeth! The thing tried to snap Dean up in its jaws!

8

How do you think Mother Dinosaur would feel if she knew about Dean's day out?

TALK ABOUT IT

FOLD

FOLD

3

Dean stuck his head out of the shell. Then he crawled out of the egg and looked around.

This book belongs to:

_____

DEAN'S DAY OUT

1

7

Dean crawled back into his shell. Mother Dinosaur came back and saw him. "What a good boy!" she said. "You can come out now."

5

A mean-looking thing flew down. It tried to catch Dean in its beak! Dean hid under a leaf.

FOLD

FOLD

Mother Dinosaur tapped each egg. "Not ready yet," she said. "I'll go look for some good green leaves to eat."

2

Everything was new to Dean. He set out to see the world.

4

Name _____

Dino sleeps outside the house.
He never makes a sound.
He doesn't eat the flowers.
He's the greatest pet in town.

▶ **Say** the name of the picture. **Find** its name in the list. **Print** its letter on the line below the picture.

1

_____

2

_____

3

_____

4

_____

a. clown   h. crown
b. cowboy   i. cloud
c. mouse   j. cow
d. shower   k. towel
e. howl   l. flowers
f. owl   m. house
g. now   n. mouth

5

_____

6

_____

7

_____

8
_____

9
_____

10
_____

1. I live on the edge of a small town.

   _____

2. My house is near a farm.

   _____

3. I spend a lot of time outdoors.

   _____

4. From my yard I can see cows and horses.

   _____

5. In the summer I watch the farmer plow his field.

   _____

6. His tractor makes a loud noise.

   _____

7. At night, I hear many different sounds.

   _____

8. I can hear owls calling.

   _____

9. I like to watch the clouds beyond the hills.

   _____

10. In the fall the flowers on the hill bloom.

    _____

11. Today I saw a flock of birds flying south.

    _____

12. They sense that winter is about to start.

    _____

THINK! Does the person in the story live in the city or the country?

Name _____

Find **a word in the box that answers each riddle.** Print **it on the line.**

owl	flower	house	plow
cow	cloud	clown	ground

1 I am in the sky.
Sometimes I bring you rain.
What am I?

_____

2 I wear a funny suit.
I do many tricks.
I can make you smile.
What am I?

_____

3 I am in the garden.
I am very colorful.
I may grow in your yard, too.
What am I?

_____

4 You can plant seeds in me.
The farmer must plow me.
What am I?

_____

5 I am wide awake in the dark.
I hoot and howl.
What am I?

_____

6 You can see me at the farm.
I eat green grass.
I give you good milk.
What am I?

_____

7 You can live in me.
I will keep you warm
and cozy.
What am I?

_____

8 The farmer uses me.
I help him make his garden.
What am I?

_____

Print an X beside each word in which ow stands for the long o sound.

1. _____ how
2. _____ snow
3. _____ own
4. _____ town

5. _____ crowd
6. _____ now
7. _____ bowl
8. _____ grow

9. _____ low
10. _____ plow
11. _____ power
12. _____ owl

13. _____ slow
14. _____ flow
15. _____ know
16. _____ show

17. _____ brown
18. _____ crow
19. _____ crown
20. _____ down

21. _____ towel
22. _____ glow
23. _____ throw
24. _____ brown

25. _____ cow
26. _____ blow
27. _____ arrow
28. _____ tower

 Circle the ow word in each sentence. Print an X in the correct column to show which sound ow makes.

	long vowel	diphthong
29. The circus came to our town.	_____	_____
30. We went to the show last night.	_____	_____
31. We sat in the very first row.	_____	_____
32. The star was a funny clown.	_____	_____
33. He made the crowd laugh.	_____	_____

Home

Help your child make cards for words 1–10 and sort them according to the long o sound.

Name _____

The diphthongs **oi** and **oy** usually stand for the same sound. You can hear that sound in **coin** and **boy**.

▶ Circle **the name of each picture.**

1

bow
boil
bill

2

boy
bag
toy

3

corn
coil
coins

4

sail
sell
soil

5

oak
oil
out

6

toil
tail
toys

7

paint
point
pail

8

noise
nail
nose

9

fame
foil
fawn

▶ Finish **each sentence with a word from the box.**

enjoy   toy   coins

10. I have saved a few dollars and some _____.

11. I will buy a _____ robot kit.

12. I will _____ putting it together.

The Runaway Toy

A boy named Roy had a birthday. His grandmother and grandfather gave him a choice of toys. Roy chose a toy train. He was a very happy boy.

Roy enjoyed his toy train, but it made too much noise. Roy took out a can of oil and oiled the toy. The oil made the train less noisy. It made it go faster, too.

One day Roy oiled it too much. The train went faster and faster. It raced around the room and out the door. Roy chased it. The toy train rolled up to his sister, Joy.

"Look," said Joy. "This toy wants to join me outside."

"That's my toy train," said Roy. "It ran away from me. From now on I will be more careful. I will not spoil my toy with too much oil."

▶ **Use the words you marked to answer the questions.**

1. What was the boy's name? _____

2. What kind of train did he get? _____

3. What made the train go fast? _____

4. What made Roy oil the train? _____

 THINK! What other toys could Roy have chosen?

 **208**

Lesson 97
Diphthongs oi, oy: Words in context

 Home Together, read and act out the story. Then switch roles.

Name _____

Find the word on the bowl that will finish each sentence. Print it on the line.

spoil	Joy
oil	choice
joins	Floyd's
boy	enjoy
toys	noise

1. Floyd is a hungry _____.

2. He does not want to play with his _____.

3. Now he would _____ a bowl of popcorn.

4. _____ friend Joy wants popcorn, too.

5. Popcorn won't _____ their dinner.

6. Joy _____ Floyd in the kitchen.

7. Floyd pours some _____ in a pan.

8. _____ tells him to be careful.

9. The children listen for a popping _____.

10. Did Floyd and Joy make a good _____?

 Do you think they made a good choice? Why?

Circle yes or no to answer each question.

1. Is a penny a coin?   Yes   No

2. Is joy being very sad?   Yes   No

3. Can you play with a toy?   Yes   No

4. Is oil used in a car?   Yes   No

5. Is a point the same as paint?   Yes   No

6. Can you boil water?   Yes   No

7. Can you make a choice?   Yes   No

8. Is a loud noise quiet?   Yes   No

Find the word in the box that will finish each sentence. Print it on the line.

| spoil |
| enjoys |
| toy |
| Joyce |
| noise |
| points |
| boy |

9. _____ is glad the circus is in town.

10. She loves the _____ of the crowd.

11. The clown rides in a _____ cart.

12. She smiles and _____ at the funny clown.

13. She sees a _____ standing up on a horse.

14. Nothing can _____ the day for Joyce.

15. Joyce always _____ a day at the circus.

Home

Take turns using the *oi* and *oy* words in new sentences.

Name _____

RULE

The diphthong **ew** stands for the long **u** sound. You can hear the long **u** sound in **new** and **few**.

grew
blew
chew
flew
new
threw
knew
few

1. I bought a _____ pack of sugarless gum.

2. I put a _____ pieces into my mouth.

3. I began to _____ the gum.

4. Then I _____ a giant bubble.

5. That bubble grew and _____.

6. Suddenly, I _____ I was in trouble.

7. The bubble broke, and pieces _____ everywhere.

8. I _____ the pieces of chewed gum away.

▶ Print **the missing letters for a word that rhymes with each word. Trace the whole word.**

9	few	10	crew	11	grew
_st___		_thr_		_fl_	

1. (Drew, Blew, Knew) wanted a pet.

2. He went to a pet shop called (crew, dew, Flew) the Coop.

3. He saw puppies (chewing, stewing, mewing) on toy bones.

4. Baby birds (flew, stew, knew) around their cage.

5. They (few, threw, grew) seeds on the floor.

6. Drew really wanted a (mew, stew, new) kitten.

7. He saw a (chew, crew, grew) of kittens.

8. A (few, threw, grew) were very cute.

9. One kitten looked at him and (flew, mewed, chewed).

10. Drew (grew, dew, knew) he wanted that kitten.

11. Drew named him (Mews, Stews, Dews) because he always mewed.

12. That kitten (new, grew, chew) bigger every day.

13. Mews liked it when Drew (few, threw, mew) a toy to him.

14. He liked to (chew, new, stew) on Drew's shoestrings.

15. Mew tried to hide under the (screws, grew, newspaper).

16. From the window he watched birds as they (flew, crew, dew).

17. When the wind (blew, drew, stew), Mews chased fallen leaves.

18. He licked drops of morning (mew, dew, chew).

19. Before Drew (threw, few, knew) it, Mews was his friend.

20. Drew really loved his (stew, new, flew) pet.

 **What do you think Drew liked best about Mews?**

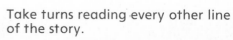

Name _____

▶ **Say** and **spell** the words in the box. **Name** each picture and **write** each word whose name has the same vowel sound. Then **circle** the letters that stand for the vowel sound.

cloud	hair	seed	wealth	lie	day
row	moon	draw	boy	soon	cow
tie	spoil	boat	peach	haul	head

1. _____

2. _____

3. _____

4. _____

5. _____

6. _____

7. _____

8. _____

9. _____

Lesson 100

213

Review vowel pairs, digraphs, diphthongs: Spelling

Phonics & Writing

Write a rhyme about dinosaurs. Use some of the words in the box. Share your rhyme with the class.

look	nail	sound	claw	know
ready	meat	found	toe	few
day	eat	green	die	new

Book Corner

Dinosaur Days
by Judy Nayer

Twins named Dawn and Paul share a love for dinosaurs, which continues even when they grow up.

Dinosaur Days
WRITTEN BY JUDY NAYER
ILLUSTRATED BY GAIL PIAZZA

Home Invite your child to read his or her poem aloud to family members.

6

Answer: He followed the tracks!

How did the dinosaur find the missing train?

FOLD

✂ 8

Which dinosaur riddle do you like best? Why?

FOLD

Answer: He wanted to see time fly!

Why did the dinosaur throw the clock out the window?

3

© MCP All rights reserved. Copying strictly prohibited.

This book belongs to:

RIDDLES

✂ 1

DINOSAUR RIDDLES

Review vowel pairs, diagraphs, diphthongs: Take-Home Book

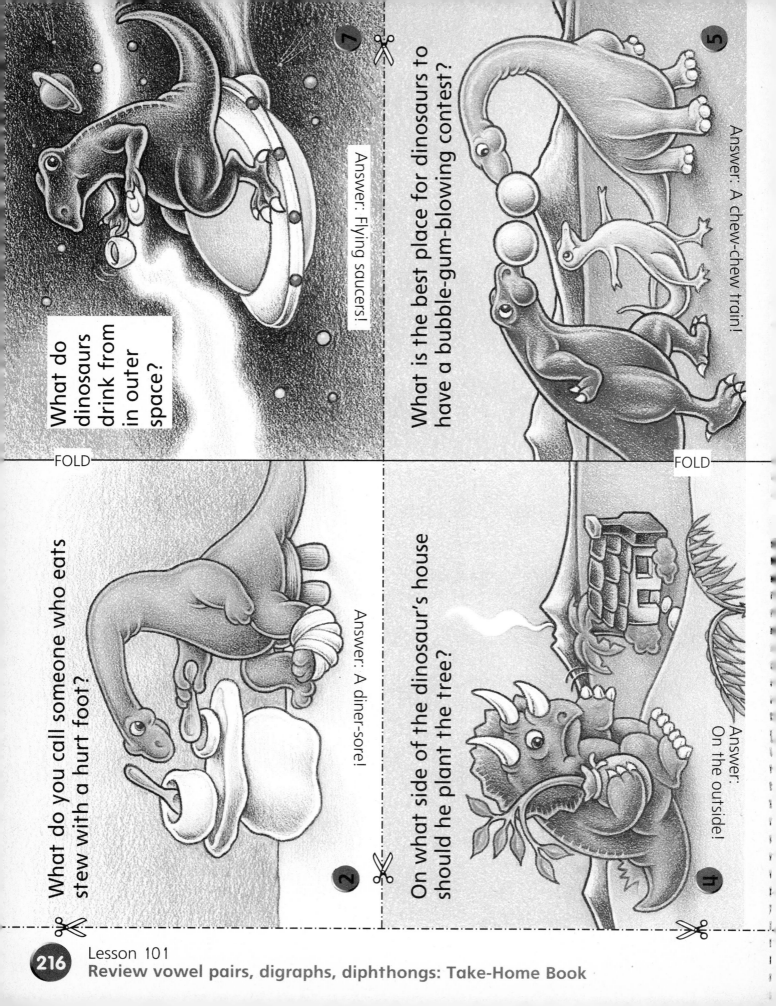

7

Answer: Flying saucers!

What do dinosaurs drink from in outer space?

5

Answer: A chew-chew train!

What is the best place for dinosaurs to have a bubble-gum-blowing contest?

FOLD

FOLD

What do you call someone who eats stew with a hurt foot?

Answer: A diner-sore!

2

On what side of the dinosaur's house should he plant the tree?

Answer: On the outside!

4

Lesson 101
Review vowel pairs, digraphs, diphthongs: Take-Home Book

UNIT 6 CHECKUP

Name _____

Circle the word that will finish each sentence. Then print it on the line.

1. A baby deer is a _____.   seal   fawn   feather

2. A deep dish is a _____.   bean   bait   bowl

3. A place where you can see

   animals is a _____.   zoo   zipper   hook

4. Dried grass that horses eat

   is _____.   seed   hay   day

5. A small animal with a long

   tail is a _____.   men   mitt   mouse

6. Something you row

   is a _____.   boat   beach   boy

7. You walk on your two

   _____.   feet   foot   flat

8. One animal that gives milk is

   a _____.   cloud   crow   cow

9. Something that was never

   used is _____.   grew   new   draw

10. A dish under a cup is a

    _____.   train   faucet   saucer

Fill in **the bubble in front of the word that will finish each sentence.**

1. Dinosaurs ___ their eggs in nests. ○ day   ○ laid   ○ paid

2. The mother ___ around the eggs. ○ coiled ○ heated ○ boiled

3. Many dinosaurs ___ huge. ○ saw   ○ drew   ○ grew

4. The giant tyrannosaurus ate ___. ○ toys   ○ meet   ○ meat

5. It had long claws on each ___. ○ toe   ○ foe   ○ hair

6. It had sharp teeth in its ___. ○ bread ○ head ○ peach

7. It caught animals
   in its strong ___. ○ draw ○ jaw   ○ haul

8. The stegosaurus had ___ of
   plates on its back. ○ rows ○ seeds ○ boats

9. It had bony spikes on its ___. ○ sail   ○ coin   ○ tail

10. No dinosaurs are alive ___. ○ cloud ○ now   ○ cow

11. They ___ long ago. ○ died ○ lied ○ boy

12. We can only guess what
    they ___ like. ○ book ○ looked ○ playing

Lesson 102
Vowel pairs, digraphs, diphthongs: Checkup

Origami

Brightly colored squares,
Appearing, disappearing,
Lovely birds unfold.

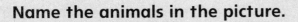

▶ **Name the animals in the picture.**

 **How are the animals made?**

Home Letter

Dear Family,

In the next few weeks your child will be learning about different kinds of words, including

Prefixes	Synonyms	Homonyms	Antonyms
read	little		

| reread | small | pear   pair | tall   short |

As we learn new words we'll also be exploring a variety of different arts and crafts, such as origami, quilting, and making play dough.

At-Home Activities

Here are some activities you and your child can do together.

▶ Gather together uncooked spaghetti and macaroni, buttons, pieces of ribbon and yarn, and pictures cut from magazines. Help your child glue these items on paper to make a collage.

▶ Read the directions for a recipe. Together, look for words to which the prefixes **re, un,** and **dis** can be added to make new words—for example: **re**heat, **un**wrap, **dis**card.

Book Corner

You and your child might enjoy reading these books together.

The Keeping Quilt
by Patricia Polacco

This is the story of a special quilt made by the author's family. Each generation adds to the quilt using scraps of clothing.

I Can Draw Dinosaurs
by Toni Tallarico

Simple circles and squares turn into lifelike dinosaurs when children follow these easy step-by-step instructions.

Sincerely,

Name _____

Don't throw out old puppets.
Recycle them instead!
Simply reglue the hair and eyes,
And just refill the head.

▶ Add **re** to the word beside each sentence. Use **the new words to finish the sentences.**

RULE
The prefix **re** usually means **do again.** Add **re** to the base word **glue** to make **reglue.**
> **Reglue** the hair and eyes.

1. Every day I do things that I have to _____. | do

2. When I get up, I _____ my bed. | make

3. I _____ my teeth after I eat. | brush

4. I _____ my backpack before school. | pack

5. I _____ my shoes. | tie

6. When my camera needs film, I _____ it. | load

7. I read and _____ my favorite books. | read

8. I write and _____ my stories. | write

9. Every night I _____ my alarm clock. | wind

THINK!
What do you do every day before school?

Add **un** to the word beside each sentence. **Use** the new words to finish the sentences.

1. Every day we do things and _____ them. | do |

2. We dress and _____. | dress |

3. We button and _____ our clothes. | button |

4. We tie our shoes and then _____ them. | tie |

5. We lock and _____ doors. | lock |

6. We buckle our seat belts and _____ them. | buckle |

7. We wrap up our lunches and then

   _____ them. | wrap |

8. We pack our backpacks and _____ them. | pack |

9. We load film in a camera and later _____ it. | load |

10. I am not _____ about all this undoing. | happy |

11. It just seems a little _____ to me. | usual |

12. But it's probably _____ things will ever change. | likely |

Home   With your child, take turns making up new sentences for the *un-* words.

Name _____

1. Last night my baby sister _____ my backpack. | **packed**

2. She tried to _____ my homework with her crayon. | **do**

3. I have to _____ my story. | **write**

4. Now I _____ my backpack every night. | **check**

5. I am very _____ about it, too. | **happy**

6. My things are _____ around my sister. | **safe**

▶ **Print** one word that means the same as each pair of words.

7. not cooked _____

8. not safe _____

9. not able _____

10. not kind _____

11. spell again _____

12. use again _____

13. play again _____

14. tell again _____

Add the prefix **un** or **re** to each underlined word. Print the new word on the line.

1 to <u>read</u> again

_____

2 opposite of <u>lock</u>

_____

3 to <u>fill</u> again

_____

4 opposite of <u>tie</u>

_____

5 opposite of <u>buckle</u>

_____

6 to <u>heat</u> again

_____

7 to <u>build</u> again

_____

8 opposite of <u>pack</u>

_____

9 to <u>write</u> again

_____

10 opposite of <u>happy</u>

_____

11 to <u>play</u> again

_____

12 to <u>wind</u> again

_____

Home Write prefixes (re-, un-) and base words on separate cards. Match them to make new words.

Name _____

► Add **dis** to the word beside each sentence.
Use **the new words to finish the sentences.**

RULE

The prefix **dis** also means the opposite of the original word. Add **dis** to the base word **order** to make **disorder.**

1. My dog Wags _____ for a while. | appeared |

2. Then I _____ my shoe was missing. | covered |

3. "Why did you _____ me, Wags?" | obey |

4. "You know I'm _____ when you take my things." | pleased |

5. "That was a _____ thing to do." | loyal |

6. "Wags, you are a _____." | grace |

7. Wags barked to _____. | agree |

8. He pulled my shoe out of my

_____ toy chest. | orderly |

THINK! What did the boy think happened to his shoe?

Lesson 105
Prefix dis-

225

Fill in the bubble beside the word that will finish each sentence. Write the word on the line.

1

Mr. Fixit will

_____

the plug before fixing the telephone.

- ○ discolor
- ○ disconnect

2

The rider will

_____

and let her horse rest.

- ○ dismount
- ○ distaste

3

Meg and Peg are twin sisters, but

they _____
about many things.

- ○ disagree
- ○ disappear

4

The puppy

_____ its
owner and ran outside with her hat.

- ○ dishonest
- ○ disobeyed

5

Will loves green beans, but he

_____

eggplant.

- ○ dislikes
- ○ disgrace

6

Kirk made the dirt appear, so he
had to make it

_____.

- ○ disappear
- ○ distrust

Lesson 105
Prefix dis-

Take turns making up sentences for
the unused *dis-* words on this page.

Name _____

▶ Add **un, dis,** or **re** to each base word to make a new word. **Print** the word on the line.

un or dis		re or dis	
1. _____ agree	2. _____ happy	7. _____ able	8. _____ writes
3. _____ obey	4. _____ easy	9. _____ new	10. _____ like
5. _____ lucky	6. _____ please	11. _____ pay	12. _____ loyal

▶ Add **un, dis,** or **re** to each underlined word to change the meaning of the sentence. **Print** the new word on the line.

13. Grandpa was <u>pleased</u> about the plans for his party.

_____

14. He said he felt <u>easy</u> about getting gifts.

_____

15. Sadly Sue <u>wrapped</u> the present she had made.

_____

16. Then Jake said they would <u>obey</u> Grandpa just once.

_____

17. With a grin, Sue <u>wrapped</u> the gift.

_____

18. She <u>tied</u> the bow.

_____

19. Grandpa was not <u>happy</u> with his party after all.

_____

Draw a line from the prefix to a base word to make a new word. Write the word on the line.

un	read
dis	happy
re	obey

1. _____

2. _____

3. _____

dis	easy
re	agree
un	pay

4. _____

5. _____

6. _____

▶ **Add un, dis, or re to the base word to make a word that will finish the sentence. Write the new word on the line.**

7.	Amber will _____ her gift.	wrap
8.	Alex and Max _____.	agree
9.	Rita will _____ the house.	build
10.	Taro is never _____ to animals.	kind
11.	Look! The ice is still _____.	safe
12.	My baby sister _____ rice.	likes
13.	The magician made the bird _____.	appear

 Home

Use the new words in the boxes at the top of the page in sentences.

Name _____

Hot or cold, rain or shine,
My dog likes the backyard best.
Day or night, summer or winter,
He needs a place to rest.

▶ **Find a word in the box that means the opposite of each word. Print its letter on the line.**

RULE

Antonyms are words that are opposite or almost opposite in meaning. **Hot** and **cold** mean the opposite of each other.

a. **old**	b. **wet**	c. **start**	d. **full**	e. **slow**
f. **last**	g. **down**	h. **hot**	i. **good**	j. **short**
k. **out**	l. **well**	m. **few**	n. **winter**	o. **long**
p. **far**	q. **lower**	r. **shallow**	s. **shut**	t. **awake**
u. **thick**	v. **fat**	w. **white**	x. **hard**	

1. ____ dry   2. ____ up   3. ____ summer   4. ____ short

5. ____ near   6. ____ fast   7. ____ tall   8. ____ bad

9. ____ cold   10. ____ thin   11. ____ sick   12. ____ many

13. ____ stop   14. ____ upper   15. ____ first   16. ____ deep

17. ____ new   18. ____ empty   19. ____ open   20. ____ in

21. ____ asleep   22. ____ easy   23. ____ black   24. ____ skinny

Print a word from the box that means the opposite of each word and describes the picture.

stop	open	full	ill	cry	night
float	hot	strong	asleep	sit	smile

1 awake

2 close

3 empty

4 cold

5 healthy

6 stand

7 weak

8 sink

9 day

10 laugh

11 frown

12 go

Lesson 108
Antonyms

Home

Take turns using each antonym pair in a sentence.

Name _____

Grandma will sew a blue-green quilt
So everyone can see
How the wind blew the boats about
On a stormy day at sea.

Find **a word in the box that sounds the same as each word below.** Print **the word on the line.**

tail	here	to	road	pail	heal
blue	week	cent	sail	maid	sea

1. heel _____

2. see _____

3. rode _____

4. sent _____

5. tale _____

6. blew _____

7. weak _____

8. pale _____

9. hear _____

10. two _____

11. sale _____

12. made _____

Circle **the word that will finish each sentence.** Print **it on the line.**

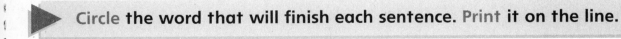

13. Maggie _____ her horse into the woods.   road   rode

14. Her puppy wagged its _____ and ran along.   tail   tale

15. They saw a _____ that hid behind a tree.   dear   deer

16. Maggie watched the _____ set in the west.   son   sun

Find a word in the box that sounds the same as each word below. Print it on the line.

son	meat	blew
to	pane	tow
tale	week	heel
wait	beet	cent
sea	dear	sew

1. weight _____

2. sun _____

3. weak _____

4. sent _____

5. blue _____

6. beat _____

7. deer _____

8. two _____

9. heal _____

10. pain _____

11. see _____

12. meet _____

13. so _____

14. tail _____

15. toe _____

Use words from the box and the activity above to finish the sentences.

16. It had rained all _____.

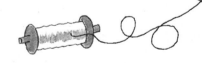

17. When Pete woke up, the _____ was shining.

18. He could _____ his friends playing outside.

19. He pulled on his _____ jeans in a hurry.

20. He ran out _____ fly his kite.

Lesson 109
Homonyms

Help your child write each homonym on a card or paper and then match them.

Phonics &
Spelling

Read the words in the box. Then write two words that belong under each heading.

Words That Mean the Same Thing

_____   _____

Words That Sound the Same

_____   _____

Words That Are Opposites

_____   _____

Words That Begin with dis-

_____   _____

Words That Begin with un-

_____   _____

Words That Begin with re-

_____   _____

Word List

rewrite
dislike
hot
little
reread
undo
cold
deer
dear
disagree
unhappy
small

Phonics & Writing

Write about your favorite color. Why do you like it? What comes in this color? How does it make you feel? **Use** some of the words in the box.

unusual
little
hot
cold
glad
disagree
dislike
hard
easy
discover

Book Corner

Making a Plate
by Jennifer Jacobson

Potter Sam Salas shows how to make a plate beginning with a lump of wet clay and ending with a finished piece.

Home

Ask your child to read his or her writing to you.

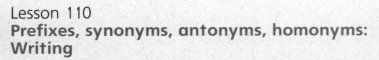

6

Roll out the dough. Don't make it too thick or too thin. Cut out shapes. They can be big or little, tall or short.

3

This is what you will need:

2 cups salt

2 cups warm water

5 cups flour

8

What would you like to make out of play dough?

TALK ABOUT IT

1

This book belongs to:

Make Your Own Play Dough

Prefixes, synonyms, antonyms, homonyms: Take-Home Book

It is unlikely you will have any dough left over. But if you do, you can reuse it later.

Knead and reknead the dough until it is smooth and even.

FOLD

FOLD

You can make your own play dough. It is easy and simple to do!

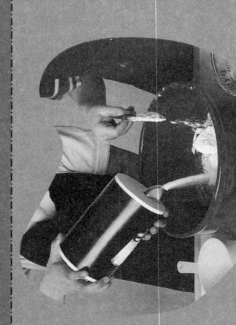

Mix the salt, flour, and water. Add a cup of water. Refill the cup and add more water if you need it.

Lesson 111
Prefixes, synonyms, antonyms, homonyms: Take-Home Book

UNIT 7 CHECKUP

Name _____

▶ **Circle two words in each box that mean the same thing.**

1 cold cool seed shook	**2** hair small little home	**3** fast fell quick queen
4 three tree shut close	**5** jump leap drink drop	**6** sick snow ill blow

▶ **Circle two words in each box that mean the opposite.**

7 little puppy jelly big	**8** fly old new penny	**9** bad candy rich good
10 they fast play slow	**11** from dirty clean funny	**12** asleep play baby awake

▶ **Circle the word that will finish each sentence. Print it on the line.**

13. The _____ was shining.   sun   son

14. I put on my _____ shorts and blue hat.   read   red

15. I went for a sail on the _____.   see   sea

16. The wind blew the _____.   sails   sales

17. It almost _____ my hat off, too.   blew   blue

18. I had a _____ time!   grate   great

Lesson 112

239

Prefixes, synonyms, antonyms, homonyms: Checkup

UNIT 7 CHECKUP

Fill in the bubble beside the word that names or describes each picture.

1
○ tale
○ tell
○ tail

2
○ heel
○ hail
○ heal

3
○ day
○ deer
○ dear

4
○ rode
○ rod
○ road

5
○ sun
○ son
○ soon

6
○ knows
○ nose
○ now

Read the words. Fill in the bubble next to the word that has the same meaning.

7 opposite of wrap
○ unwrap
○ rewrap

8 to play again
○ replay
○ display

9 opposite of mount
○ dismount
○ remount

10 opposite of appear
○ reappear
○ disappear

11 spell again
○ dispell
○ respell

12 to tie again
○ untie
○ retie

13 opposite of like
○ dislike
○ relike

14 opposite of do
○ redo
○ undo

15 to pack again
○ repack
○ unpack

Lesson 112
Prefixes, synonyms, antonyms, homonyms: Checkup